MISSION LAUNCH
Team Training

A Training Curriculum for
International Short-Term Mission Teams
(Teams traveling outside the United States or Canada)

Member Guide
Version: Intl-1.1

Written By
Eric and Carol Hanson

MISSION
EXCELL

www.missiontriptraining.com

MISSION LAUNCH TEAM TRAINING

A Training Curriculum for International Short-Term Mission Teams
(Teams traveling outside the United States or Canada)

Member Guide

Version Intl-1.1

Copyright © 2007 by Eric and Carol Hanson.

This Team Member Guide is designed to be used in conjunction with a Mission Launch Team Training Leader Guide in a group setting. Each team member is to have their <u>own</u> Team Member Guide for <u>each</u> mission trip. Any children/teenagers traveling with their parent(s) should have their own Team Member Guide as well. To order more Guides, please visit our website: www. missiontriptraining.com.

Video Production: Kiwimonkie Films (www.kiwimonkie.com)

Cover Design: Carol Hanson

ISBN 978-1-60585-763-3

Printed in the United States of America

This Team Member Guide Belongs To:

_____

Trip Destination:

_____

Trip Dates:

_____

Place Team Photo Here

Acknowledgements

We are grateful to everyone who contributed to this curriculum, including: Kiwimonkie Films for the outstanding video production; Kate Callan for your curriculum suggestions; Eric Liechty for your design ideas; our parents for your love, prayers, and generosity; and Doug Yonamine and Jerry Trousdale for your wisdom and advice as we entered the publishing world.

To our family, friends, supporters, and pastors over the years: thank you for your encouragement, support, and prayers as we have traveled this adventure in missions. To Dwight Marable: thank you for believing in that young couple who showed up at your doorstep with their U-Haul trailer in 1996.

We are particularly indebted to some of the original short-term mission planning books, such as *Vacations with a Purpose, Successful Mission Teams, and The Essential Guide to the Short Term Mission Trip*, which inspired some of the material written in this Guide.

Finally, we want to thank all of those team members who have traveled with us on past trips. We have learned so much from you. Thank you for the privilege of seeing God use you to impact the nations!

This curriculum is dedicated to our Lord and Savior, Jesus Christ. May a passion for His Kingdom be ignited in everyone who prays, gives, or goes on this trip.

CONTENTS

ON THE FIELD

DEBRIEF AND RE-ENTRY MEETING

APPENDIX

WELCOME

WELCOME

You are about to embark on an exciting journey with God! You may have heard stories from friends who went on similar trips and came home changed. Well, God has a plan for you too, and it is going to be awesome!

You may not realize it but YOU are an answer to our prayers. Jesus said to his disciples...

> *"The harvest is plentiful but the workers are few. Ask the Lord of the harvest, therefore, to send out workers into his harvest field."*
> *Matthew 9:37-38*

The "harvest" is plentiful. People are hungry for the message of Good News all around this world and we continuously pray that God would send out workers into the "harvest fields." You've heard that call of God and responded – and answered our prayers! Praise God!

Your Team Member Guide

This Team Member Guide is provided to you as a resource to help you prepare for your upcoming trip. It contains critical information to prepare you spiritually, cross-culturally, relationally, and physically so that your whole team can be effective in another culture, as well as when you return home.

Bring your Team Member Guide with you to every team meeting - inside it, you will find sections to take notes during each meeting. During these meetings, you will be bonding with your teammates, learning how to communicate cross-culturally, and hopefully, deepening your dependence and trust in Jesus.

In-between meetings, you will have Self-Study material to complete in your Team Member Guide. On the field, it will serve as your daily devotional and journal and will help prepare you for your return home.

Your Team Member Guide will become a remembrance for you. You will be making notes and journaling as you prepare, serve on the field, and come home. At the end of your trip, be sure to place a photo of your team in the front of your Team Member Guide. Years later, you can look back and remember what God did in your life through this mission trip!

Get Ready!

We guarantee that if you are willing to step out of your "comfort zone" and serve others in whatever way is needed – God will use you in ways you could never have imagined. Get ready to have your faith ignited as the Holy Spirit works through you to impact other people!

> *I will praise you, O Lord, among the nations; I will sing of you among the peoples. For great is your love, reaching to the heavens; your faithfulness reaches to the skies. Be exalted, O God, above the heavens; let your glory be over all the earth.*
>
> *Psalm 57: 9-11*

TEAM MEETING ONE

TEAM MEETING ONE

Introduction

Welcome and Prayer

Getting Focused

Bible Verse

What can we learn from these verses?

How can we apply this to our lives and our mission?

Introductions

- Name
- Family information
- Reason for joining the team
- Icebreaker question

My Team Members:

1. _Nathan_
2. _Alex_
3. _Joshua_
4. _Caly - Ramsing -_
5. _Beeky_
6. _Ryan_
7. _Erica / Anthony Bond_
8. _Cindy - Chinese daughter (ASL) Valerie_
9. _Brian -_
10. ~~Kristian~~ _Kristina_
11. _- Leslie, Dan, Daniel Mansfield_
12. _↳ military → Haiti_
13. _-_
14.
15.
16.
17.
18.
19.
20.

Vision for the Mission

Notes:

Read: Matthew 28:18-20

What is the mission of this team?

Who is being discipled on this trip?

Read: Philemon 6

What's the difference between knowing about something and actually doing it?

Trip Timeline

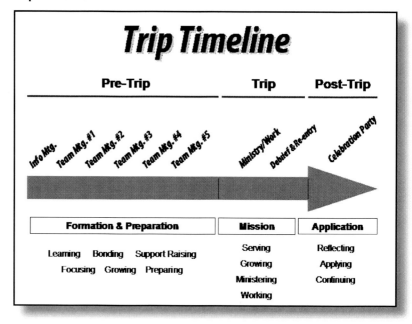

Notes:

Team Building

Activity: Group vs. Team

Why do we want to be a TEAM vs. a GROUP of individuals?

Version: ML Intl-1.1

Team Covenant

Short-term mission teams are extremely dynamic in nature and are designed to bring team members closer to God while making Christ known throughout the world. Team members should be able to experience the diversity of the worldwide Body of Christ, to expand their vision, and to participate in fruitful ministry that has long-lasting impact. In order for this to occur, we must agree upon how we will act – our attitudes and expectations. If we do this, the potential is out of this world! Please read and sign the following Team Covenant.

"As a member of this team, I agree to the following:"

1) **Spiritual Growth:** I will be open to learn from God's Spirit in all situations. I will have regular Bible devotion and prayer times with God before the trip and daily on the trip, because I believe that growing individually is essential to growing as a team.

2) **Teamwork:** I commit myself to be a team member who brings unity. I am willing to sacrifice my own agenda and personal luxuries for the sake of the team. I commit to resolve all intra-team conflicts according to biblical principles. This involves prayer as the first step, personal confrontation in love as the next step, and the counsel of a third party, namely the team leader, as a third and final resort (Matthew 18:15-17).

3) **Team Preparation/Meetings:** I commit to participating in all team meetings before, during, and after the trip. Team meetings will include team devotions, team prayer, time for communicating details and plans, and time for individual relational development and training. I also commit to preparing for these team meetings – completing self-study homework and assigned reading.

4) **Positive Attitude:** I commit to encourage my teammates and build them up throughout our trip. I will refrain from complaining. I realize that each team member will be looked upon as an example of how a Christian should act and I will not treat that responsibility lightly. I promise to adopt a flexible attitude and be supportive, as plans may need to be changed. I will be a "positive" and not a "negative" on the team. I will come with an expectant heart to enjoy this experience and have fun!

5) **Ministry and Work Opportunities:** I will seek to be an example of the love of Jesus to the people we meet throughout our trip. This includes giving testimonies, actively participating in ministry/work opportunities, and exhibiting Christ-like behavior (John 4:35 and 1 Corinthians 10:31). I am willing to be a servant and make myself available in any type of endeavor as needed.

6) **Health and Personal Risk:** I commit to take full responsibility for my own health during this entire mission experience and I will prepare myself spiritually, mentally, and physically – including getting the suggested immunizations. I commit to know my own limitations, understanding that I will not be forced to participate in an activity that I feel is out of my physical abilities. I will take full responsibility for my own personal safety and health.

7) **Leadership:** I recognize that the team leader is the one placed in authority and I am willing to submit to his/her leadership both when I agree and especially when I disagree with his/her decisions (Hebrews 13:17). I understand that cross-cultural

ministry can be a little tricky and that there may be several situations where I do not fully understand what is going on; it is especially in these situations, that I will choose to cooperate and submit to my team leader.

8) **Guest:** I recognize that I am an invited guest of our host ministry. Therefore, I will conduct myself in a way as to honor my hosts. I will be careful not to offend them by what I wear, eat, drink, do, and/or say. I will follow Jesus' instructions: "When you enter a town and are welcomed, eat what is set before you." (Luke 10:8) I also acknowledge that Christianity looks very different around the world and that one of the benefits of this trip is to experience how other cultures live out their faith.

9) **Relationships:** I agree to be sensitive in how I relate to members of the opposite sex, both on the team as well as those to whom we are going to work/minister. I will not pursue relations beyond basic friendships and I am willing to receive honest correction from my team leader and/or host if my behavior becomes inappropriate.

10) **Consequences:** I agree that in the event my conduct is considered so unsatisfactory that it jeopardizes the success of the trip and that if mediation during the trip has failed to correct my behavior – I will return home immediately at my own expense.

11) **Witness:** I agree not to use any illegal drugs or consume any alcoholic beverages while on this mission trip. I understand that if I do, I might not only be breaking the law, but I might also be jeopardizing my witness and could be a stumbling block for someone (team leaders will provide further parameters/explanations regarding the consumption of alcohol based upon your host's culture and expectations).

12) **Prayer and Finances:** I commit to raise the necessary prayer and financial support for the trip. I understand that my payments must be made on the dates set by the team leader and that my trip cost is my complete and personal responsibility. If I am unable to raise or pay the finances for my trip cost, the church or organization with which I am traveling is NOT responsible for paying the amount due.

Sign below, after reading together as a team:

Name: _____

Date: _____

> *I have given them the glory that you gave me, that they may be one as we are one: I in them and you in me. May they be brought to complete unity to let the world know that you sent me and have loved them even as you have loved me."* John 17:22-23

> *May the God who gives endurance and encouragement give you a spirit of unity among yourselves as you follow Christ Jesus, so that with one heart and mouth you may glorify the God and Father of our Lord Jesus Christ.* Romans 15:5-6

Roles and Resources

Leadership Opportunities

Ministry is the integration of our faith with action. It is reaching out in love and sharing the truth of the gospel in many ways - ultimately to draw people into their own personal relationship with Jesus.

Preparing for the ministry/work that we'll be doing is one of the most important parts of the team training. The more prepared we are, the more effective we will be. Opportunities to minister can arise at any time on the trip - not just at the 'scheduled' times.

> *"Always be prepared to give an answer to everyone who asks you to give the reason for the hope that you have."* 1 Peter 3:15b

Sub-Leader Roles Needed for this Trip:

Support Raising

- Prayer support is mandatory
- Financial support is highly suggested
- Checks made out to: _____
- Checks mailed back to team member
- Team member brings payments to team meetings

Notes:

See the "Support Raising Packet" in the Appendix (page 145) to get started.

Logistics

Payment and Meeting Schedule

(See next page)

Assignments

- Complete trip application
- Pay deposit
- Apply for passport, if needed
- Work through the Support Raising Packet (see Appendix) and begin sending support letters
- Read and complete Self-Study One in Team Member Guide
- Pray and contact your team leader regarding your desire to serve in a sub-leader role
- Pray for your team

Closing Prayer

Payment and Meeting Schedule

Tear out this page and place in a prominent place as a reminder!

Payment #1

Due Date: _____

Amount: _____   *(Mtg. #2 - ½ of trip cost minus deposit)*

Payment #2

Due Date: _____

Amount: _____   *(10 days prior to departure date – remainder of trip cost)*

Team Meeting #2

Date: _____   *(8-10 weeks prior to departure)*

Time: _____

Location: _____

Team Meeting #3

Date: _____   *(5-7 weeks prior to departure)*

Time: _____

Location: _____

Team Meeting #4

Date: _____   *(3-4 weeks prior to departure)*

Time: _____

Location: _____

Team Meeting #5

Date: _____   *(1-2 weeks prior to departure)*

Time: _____

Location: _____

Celebration Party

Date: _____   *(Approximately 2 weeks after return home)*

Time: _____

Location: _____

SELF-STUDY ONE

SELF-STUDY ONE

Introduction

Welcome to the adventure of short-term missions! God wants to do great things in you and through you. Thank you in advance for your diligence in completing these Self-Study lessons prior to each team meeting. Your willingness to prepare will directly correlate to how effective your team will be "on the field." Your team is counting on you!

In these Self Studies, you will be reading information pertinent to the trip and working through some questions to help you prepare. Each of these studies will take about 30 minutes to complete, so please set aside time in your schedule to be faithful to complete your studies.

You have started to get to know your team members. Now it's time to get more prepared individually!

To Complete Before Your Next Team Meeting

Please complete these items for your next meeting. Your team leader will be asking if these items are completed.

❑ Complete trip application

❑ Pay deposit

❑ Apply for passport, if needed

❑ Work through the Support Raising Packet (see Appendix) and begin sending support letters

❑ Read and complete Self-Study One in Team Member Guide

❑ Pray and contact your team leader regarding your desire to serve in a sub-leader role

❑ Pray for your team!

Exercise: Preparation Questionnaire

The following questionnaire[i] is designed to assess your current condition and prepare you in the following areas: physical, spiritual, relational, and cross-cultural. It will also help you define your motivations and expectations for this particular trip. Prayerfully and honestly working through these questions will help prepare you for what the Lord will do through you and in you on this trip!

> *Search me, O God, and know my heart; test me and know my anxious thoughts. See if there is any offensive way in me, and lead me in the way everlasting. Psalm 139:23-24*

Physical Preparation

I would rate my current state of physical health as: 1   2   3   (4)   5
                                                        Poor   Excellent

Considering the nature of this trip (climate, activity, schedule, etc.), some practical things I can do to improve my health prior to leaving are:

Spiritual Preparation

I have a desire to read the Bible.   1   2   3   4   (5)
                                      Low   High

I have a desire to spend time in prayer.   1   2   3   4   (5)
                                            Low   High

I have a desire to be used by God.   1   2   3   4   (5)
                                      Low   High

I can see God working in my life's circumstances.   1   2   3   (4)   5
                                                     Low   High

I am responsive to God's direction in my life.   1   (2)   3   4   5
                                                  Low   High

To better prepare spiritually for this trip, I need to:

Pray more

Relational Preparation

I am willing to open my heart to others.　　　1　2　3　4　(5)
　　　　　　　　　　　　　　　　　　　　　　Low　　　　　　High

The following issues influence whether or not I will open my heart to others:

- Iven of faith - fear

I often think of others before myself.　　　1　2　(3)　4　5
　　　　　　　　　　　　　　　　　　　　　　Low　　　　　　High

I am willing to give up my personal agenda for the sake of a team.　1　2　3　4　(5)
　　　　　　　　　　　　　　　　　　　　　　Low　　　　　　High

Cross-Cultural Preparation

I am aware of the different cultures around me daily.　1　2　3　4　(5)
　　　　　　　　　　　　　　　　　　　　　　Low　　　　　　High

I respond well when I'm in the minority.　　　1　2　3　4　(5)
　　　　　　　　　　　　　　　　　　　　　　Low　　　　　　High

Personal Motivation

My main motivation for going on this trip is:

To be used by God w/ my boys.

Expectations

Three expectations I have for this trip are:

1. *Gods presence*

2. *God uses my sons w/me*

3. *Gods peace for us*

Opportunities for Spiritual Preparation

Below are some opportunities and ideas that will facilitate your spiritual preparation for this trip:

Support Raising

Part of your spiritual preparation is the raising of funds and prayer support. If you are raising your funds for your trip, this may be your first opportunity to rely on God in a new way. Consider support raising as an opportunity to grow in your faith! This is an opportunity to share your faith with believers and unbelievers alike. See the "Support Raising Packet" in the Appendix, page 145, for more information.

Increased Prayer

Prayer is extremely important before and during this trip. As a team member, you should be praying for this trip and for your team members on a daily basis. During the trip, your team will pray together and may have some extended prayer times, 24-hour prayer watches, prayer walks, and other times of focused prayer. Exercise your "prayer muscles" now!

In addition, all team members should have their own individual prayer team praying for them before, during, and after the trip. Start recruiting these people immediately.

> *"The prayer of a righteous man is powerful and effective."*
> *James 5:16b*

Devotions

Devotions are very beneficial for the spiritual growth of team members individually, as well as the team as a whole. If you are not already doing so, we encourage you to do a devotion and have your own time with God every day. Get into this practice before the trip and you will reap the rewards.

Your Team Member Guide includes daily devotionals in the "On The Field" section for you to complete during your trip. Your team/devotional leader should set up a daily devotional schedule and let you know which verses you will be studying as a team. Each day, you will complete your devotional on your own and then meet with your team for discussion. Your prayerful participation in team devotions will build unity among your fellow teammates as you seek God together.

Journaling

Before and during your trip, we encourage everyone to journal your thoughts, impressions, and reflections. A journal is often best written as a prayer to God, in which you share your experiences from the trip. This will be incredibly beneficial to you as you share your trip experience with others, as well as when you personally reread your journal in the future. Your Team Member Guide includes daily journal pages in the "On The Field" section for you to use during your trip.

Your Personal Story

During one of our team meetings, we will focus on how to share our personal story (often referred to as our "testimony"). You will need to write a brief (3 minute) personal story to use on the trip. It should include your life/circumstance before God intervened, how you trusted Jesus with your life/circumstance, and your life/circumstance now, including details of your devotional life. You will have the opportunity to share this while on the trip and we want you to be used by God!

> *"Always be prepared to give an answer to everyone who asks you to give the reason for the hope that you have." 1 Peter 3:15b*

> *"They overcame him [Satan] by the blood of the Lamb and by the word of their testimony." Revelation 12:11a*

Bible Reading

Your preparation should include daily Bible reading. Keep in mind that the church/ministry/organization with whom your team will be working will quite possibly have the look and feel of the early church as described in the book of Acts. To gain that perspective, we suggest that you start reading through the book of Acts prior to your departure. Ask God to build your faith as you read it and ask the Holy Spirit to teach you as you read and process the text.

Your team leader may also assign or suggest additional reading material for your particular trip.

> *"But the Counselor, the Holy Spirit, whom the Father will send in my name, will teach you all things and will remind you of everything I have said to you." John 14:26*

Version: ML Intl-1.1

Scripture Memorization

> *"Pay attention and listen to the sayings of the wise; apply your heart*
> *to what I teach, for it is pleasing when you keep them in your heart*
> *and have all of them ready on your lips." Proverbs 22:17-18*

Memorizing scripture is a necessity for any follower of Christ. As believers, we should memorize basic scripture that could lead someone to Christ. We highly encourage you to memorize the following verses:

- *Romans 3:23 - "for all have sinned and fall short of the glory of God"*

- *Romans 6:23a - "For the wages of sin is death,"*

- *John 3:16 - "For God so loved the world that he gave his one and only Son, that whoever believes in him shall not perish but have eternal life."*

- *Ephesians 2:8a - "For it is by grace you have been saved, through faith"*

- *Romans 10:9 - "That if you confess with your mouth, 'Jesus is Lord,' and believe in your heart that God raised him from the dead, you will be saved."*

- *2 Corinthians 5:17 - "Therefore, if anyone is in Christ, he is a new creation; the old has gone, the new has come!"*

Leading Someone to Make a Decision for Christ

There are several ways to actually share the Gospel with someone. Walking someone through the "Romans Road" is one way to share the good news. To make it even easier, write the next verse's reference in your own Bible (i.e. After Romans 3:10 in your Bible, write a small "5:12"; after Romans 5:12, write "6:23", etc.). This will make it easier to you to "walk" someone down the road to Jesus.

- Romans 3:10
- Romans 5:12
- Romans 6:23
- Romans 5:8
- Romans 10:13
- Romans 10:9-10

Drawing out a visual (such as the "Bridge Diagram" in the Appendix, page 158) can be a concise way to visually share the gospel message as well.

Team Member Responsibility

To be a successful player on the team, there are some areas of responsibility that you'll need to take upon yourself. Take a moment to re-read your Team Covenant (in Team Meeting One) and make notes of any questions that you might want to ask your team leader at the next meeting.

Pray

- Praise God for who He is
- Praise God for what He is going to do through you and the team
- Ask God to open your heart to take steps of faith and trust Him.
- Pray for your team
- Pray for your team leader
- Pray for the people to whom you are going to work/minister

TEAM MEETING TWO

TEAM MEETING TWO

Introduction

Welcome and Prayer

Getting Focused

Bible Verse

What can we learn from these verses?

How can we apply this to our lives and our mission?

Self-Study Review

Notes:

Date: _____
Time: _____
Location: _____
Payment Due: _____
(½ of trip cost minus deposit)

Team Building

Activity: Team Building Game

What did I learn about myself?

Spiritual Preparation

Conduits for God

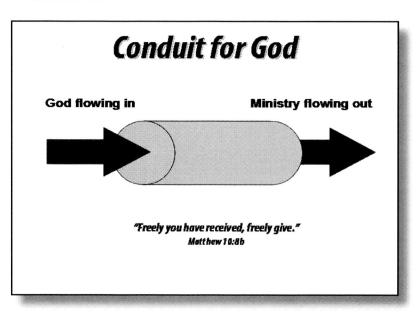

Notes:

What obstacles are present in my life that keep me from being a better conduit for God?

How can I overcome those obstacles?

Opportunities for Spiritual Preparation

Support Raising

Increased Prayer

Devotions

Journaling

Your Personal Story

Bible Reading

Additional reading assignments, if applicable:

Scripture Memorization

Leading Someone to Make a Decision for Christ

Roles and Resources

Leadership Opportunities

Leadership Roles	Names of Sub-Leaders
1. _____	1. _____
2. _____	2. _____
3. _____	3. _____
4. _____	4. _____
5. _____	5. _____
6. _____	6. _____
7. _____	7. _____
8. _____	8. _____
9. _____	9. _____
10. _____	10. _____

Logistics

Details

Assignments

- Complete visa application, if needed
- Send support letters
- Read and complete Self-Study Two in Team Member Guide
- Read Country/Local Ministry Handout, if applicable
- Begin getting any necessary immunizations
- Start extra reading assignment, if applicable
- Send thank you/update to supporters, as needed
- Pray for your team!

Closing Prayer

SELF-STUDY TWO

SELF-STUDY TWO

Introduction

God is going to use you on this trip as you make yourself available to Him. We want to challenge you to be bold, have faith, and expect God to do great things on this trip!

To Complete Before Your Next Team Meeting

Please complete these items for your next meeting. Your team leader will be asking if these items are completed.

❑ Complete visa application, if needed

❑ Send support letters

❑ Read and complete Self-Study Two in Team Member Guide

❑ Read Country/Local Ministry Handout, if applicable

❑ Begin getting any necessary immunizations

❑ Start extra reading assignment, if applicable

❑ Send thank you/update to supporters, as needed

❑ Pray for your team!

Immunizations

When traveling away from home, we all need to take some medical/health precautions. There are viruses, bacteria, and parasites to which our bodies are not accustomed and these can affect us if we are not wise and take precautions. If this trip is going to a location where there is an unusually high health risk – one that is beyond "normal" international travel – your team leader should let you know.

Keep in mind that your health is your responsibility. Your team leader can make recommendations; however, ultimately the decision of which immunizations you receive is a decision for you and your health professional. **Please make an appointment soon to visit your local travel/health clinic or personal doctor to discuss the location of your trip and the recommended immunizations and/or medicines.**

Most medical professionals and travel clinics will refer to the Center of Disease Control website (visit Mission Excell's website - www.missiontriptraining.com - for a link to CDC). Before you visit your medical professional, we recommend the following:

1. Become familiar with the specific nature of the trip and the specific location within the country of your destination.

2. Educate yourself by viewing the CDC website listed above.

3. Contact your personal health insurance provider to see if the preventative immunizations will be covered by your insurance.

Depending on the nature and location of your trip, the immunizations can vary greatly. **Start this process immediately** and remember that it is better to make the financial investment in your health than to contend with a sickness that may affect you during and after the trip.

Exercise: Preparing for Cultural Differences[ii]

From one man he made every nation of men, that they should in-habit the whole earth; and he determined the times set for them and the exact places where they should live. Acts 17:26

When I think of someone from the host culture, the following five words come to mind (be honest):

1. _____

2. _____

3. _____

4. _____

5. _____

Put a "+" by those that you perceive to be positive and a "—" by those that you perceive to be negative.

What do my answers tell me about how I view those from another culture?

What five stereotypes might the hosts have of those from my own culture?

1. _____

2. _____

3. _____

4. _____

5. _____

Put a "+" by those that you perceive to be positive and a "—" by those that you perceive to be negative.

It is natural to have a different view of those from other cultures. We are humans who are greatly influenced by our cultural background and life experiences. The good news is that simply acknowledging that we hold certain stereotypes can help us move past them! We can learn to build bridges of relationship with those from other cultures, instead of building walls of alienation.

What happens when we do not want or do not try to build bridges with those from another culture?

How can it affect the team?

How can it personally affect the hosts?

How can it affect the ongoing work of the ministry on location?

What can I do to tear down walls and build bridges instead?

Culture Shock[iii]

Traveling to another culture can be exciting, yet frustrating. Life moves much slower in most other cultures, especially in developing nations. You may feel like you have entered a time warp. The pace, along with the cultural gap, may cause you to experience "culture shock." The following information will help prepare you for entering the culture and sub-cultures of other countries, as well as helping to define the phenomenon known as "culture shock." You are traveling to another culture, ethnically speaking. And it is quite possible that you are also traveling to a different culture, spiritually speaking. The spiritual differences may include various religions other than Christianity, as well as other expressions and sub-cultures of the Christian faith.

Culture shock can be experienced without traveling abroad. It is the reaction that you have when entering a world different from your own. This tension, confusion and frustration affects people in varying degrees and people respond in unique ways. Some people can become irritable, anxious, weepy or depressed. Others may withdraw from the group as they cope with a new culture. Culture shock can only really be appreciated once it's experienced.

Below are some suggestions on how to combat "culture shock:"

- **Positive Attitude:** Prepare yourself to have a positive attitude in all situations. If you can, attempt to see things through the eyes of your hosts. A wise man once said, "Where you stand will determine what you see." Try to stand in the shoes of the people from the host country and see what they see.

- **Read:** Pick up some reading material on your destination, its people, and its customs before you leave for your trip.

- **Immerse yourself now:** Prepare by immersing yourself now! Find an ethnic neighborhood and visit their grocery store or visit another Christian church whose primary language is not English. Rent a movie in a foreign language and turn off the subtitles.

- **Give each other space:** If you notice a team member experiencing culture shock, give them space to sort things out while praying for them. You might offer to listen to what they are feeling at the time, but be careful – do not try to be the "answer-man."

- **Engage in the culture:** During the trip, try the food and ask questions of the people. Be a learner — someone who is willing to come and receive the people into your own heart. Absolutely <u>NO jokes</u> about the food, hotel, the people, differences in cultures, hand gestures, etc. Often your hosts will overhear jokes that are in bad taste and take offense.

- **Adjust your expectations:** Patience is a virtue. Whatever expectations you have, be <u>flexible</u>. Stress from being in another culture and travel weariness can wear down your emotional reserves.

- **Be flexible:** Prepare for change! Please be advised that your trip schedule should be viewed as a rough draft that will be finalized each day according to the opportunities and needs of the day. One guarantee that comes with any trip: at some point during your experience, you will be stretched outside your comfort zone, which will create more dependency upon Jesus!

- **Look beyond the "task at hand:"** In our typical "American culture," we can get self-centered quite easily. It's good to be reminded that this trip is not about us, nor is it about the activities that we plan on accomplishing. In fact, we might not complete <u>any</u> of the activities that we are planning!

- **Pray:** Find an individual on whom to focus your prayer and attention. Push beyond your own sense of need or frustration and see how God can use you to be a solution to someone who has a greater need. Take advantage of this opportunity and ask God to grow you spiritually.

Missionary life is filled with the unexpected and unplanned. Beginning to pray now can open avenues of grace and power not only to endure, but also to be filled with joy and able to release God's love and hope to people.

Our desire is that this trip will be a life-changing experience - and it *will*!

Global Expressions of the Christian Faith – Part One

Whether we realize it or not, our experiences form a frame of reference or a "lens" through which we view and interpret new information. Traveling to another culture is an opportunity to stretch that "lens" in many ways: We will eat unique foods, interact with people who have a radically different worldview, and be exposed to a religious culture that may be very different from our own.

Based upon our experiences, we each have our own "lens" through which we view the Christian Church. As humans, we have a tendency to assume that what we've experienced as "church" is correct or "the right way to do things." However, we must be careful to distinguish between the Biblical Church model and our country's modern-day culture that surrounds the church. Reading through the first few chapters of the Book of Acts will help you do this. As you read, ask yourself, "If I didn't have any past church/Christian experience, what would be my interpretation of how the church should function? What should it look like, based upon what I've read?"

The truth is – the Biblical Church model looks different in various parts of the world and it is a privilege to witness the diversity of the Body of Christ. Denominations with the same name as those in your hometown for instance, can look and feel very different in other countries.

For example, pastors who might dress very conservatively, in our eyes, may be very contemporary and charismatic – or vice-versa. A Presbyterian church may look more like a typical Pentecostal church in the States. A Lutheran church may look more like an Orthodox church. A church whose pastor is illiterate and/or uneducated, may be more scripturally based than a church in that same country that is many years old, has a well-educated pastor, and an elaborate building.

We must be careful not to judge by appearances, but to listen, observe, and pray. Expect to experience something new, different, and beautiful as your lens is broadened and your understanding of Christ's Church deepens. Appreciating the Church globally is appreciating the Bride of Christ.

Pray

- Praise God for who He is
- Praise God for what He is going to do through you and the team
- Pray for your team
- Pray for your team leader
- Pray for the people to whom you are going to work/minister

TEAM MEETING THREE

TEAM MEETING THREE

Introduction

Welcome and Prayer

Getting Focused

Bible Verse

Date: _____

Time: _____

Location: _____

Payment Due: _____

What can we learn from these verses?

How can we apply this to our lives and our mission?

Self-Study Review

Notes:

Cross-Cultural Experience

Activity: Cultural Awareness

Notes:

Trip Timeline

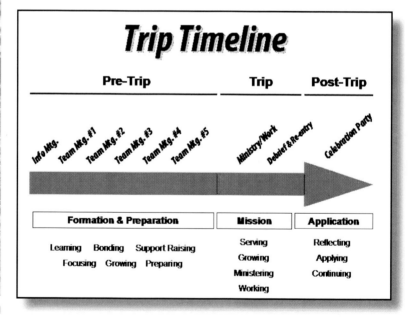

Entering another culture is like playing a game – thinking you know the rules – and then finding out that the rules are totally different than what you expected! It will be difficult to fully appreciate this phenomenon until it has been experienced firsthand; however, we can talk about the dynamics involved and prepare ourselves for this experience.

Cultural Adjustment

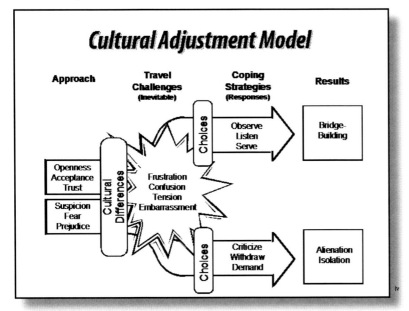

Travel Challenges

How would I respond if....

- My luggage gets lost and I don't have any clean clothes for 4 days?

- I get separated from the team during travel and end up in a location where I don't speak the language and don't know anybody?

- I've been asked to preach for an hour at the church service - right now?

- I have to skip a meal because the host forgot to make arrangements?

- When I finally do eat, the food looks and smells like a third grader's science project?

- I don't like the team leader, nor do I agree with his/her decisions?

- There is no toilet seat on the toilet?

- There is no toilet at all?

- I find a mouse in my room?

- I find a cockroach in my bed and hundreds invade my room when the lights go out?

- I have no electricity or hot water in my room?

- I have to eat rice and vegetables for 10 days straight?

- I get sick or injured?

Which road am I on in my approach?

Which road or coping strategy will I choose to take?

Culture Shock[v]

What is the definition of culture shock?

Suggestions to combat culture shock include:

• Positive Attitude

• Read

• Immerse yourself now

• Give each other space

• Engage in the culture

• Adjust your expectations

• Be flexible

• Look beyond the "task at hand"

• Pray

Missionary life is filled with the unexpected and unplanned. Beginning to pray now can open avenues of grace and power not only to endure, but also to be filled with joy and able to release God's love and hope to people.

Our desire is that this trip will be a life changing experience - and it will!

Activity: "Now What?"

How could this trip possibly be a success if we don't accomplish any of the activities that we are planning?

> *"Consider it pure joy, my brothers, whenever you face trials of many kinds, because you know that the testing of your faith develops perseverance. Perseverance must finish its work so that you may be mature and complete, not lacking anything." James 1:2-4*

Global Expressions of the Christian Faith – Part Two

Nearly 70% of all Christians live in the non-western world (other than Europe and North America). Most of them also live in the southern hemisphere where the church is "generally enthusiastic, spontaneous, fundamentalist and supernaturalist." [vi] This independent, nondenominational church has increased ten-fold in the 21st century and consists mostly of Pentecostals and Charismatics. [vii] According to these statistics, it may be likely that the Christian leaders, pastors, and churches that you will be serving and working alongside will be charismatic in nature.

Pentecostals get their name from their emphasis on the events that happened on Pentecost as recorded in Acts 2. They believe that the Holy Spirit comes upon believers today as well, and that being "baptized in the Holy Spirit" is part of the Christian experience. Pentecostals hold a special emphasis on the spiritual gift of speaking in tongues as a sign of someone upon whom the Holy Spirit has fallen ("upon" = *epi* in the Greek).

Charismatics, [which is derived from the word charisma (khar'-is-mah) a (spiritual) endowment, miraculous faculty and/or gift [viii]], also believe that the manifestations of the Holy Spirit are alive and well in the Church today. These are the gifts Paul wrote about to the church in Corinth (1 Corinthians 12:4-11 and chapter 14): wisdom, words of knowledge, faith, healing, miraculous powers, prophecy, distinguishing between spirits, speaking in different kinds of tongues, and the interpretation of tongues. Like Pentecostals, charismatics would also believe that a subsequent (although sometimes simultaneous) event occurs where the Holy Spirit comes upon (*epi* in the Greek) an individual to empower the believer for ministry by releasing the gifts. They most often will emphasize the gift of speaking in tongues as well; however, unlike most Pentecostals, charismatics do not typically believe that the gifts (i.e. speaking in tongues) must be active in someone's life for them to be "born-again." Charismatics will not usually form their own separate denomination; but rather view themselves as a "force of renewal within existing Protestant and Roman Catholic churches." [ix]

So, what will we experience? We may hear people speaking in tongues (Acts 2:4) in the worship services or praying in an unknown language (other than the local language). The music may be quite different from that which we are familiar. It may be quite loud and the worshippers may raise their hands and enthusiastically worship God for a much longer duration than in our normal experience. Dancing as part of worship may be experienced as well.

People may be prayed for personally during the church services through the "laying on of hands (Luke 4:40; Mark 16:18b; Acts 6:6; Act 19:6; 1 Timothy 4:14)." We might have the opportunity to participate in praying for others individually or in small groups. Usually the nationals we are ministering to are eager for team members to pray for them individually. In the context of your trip, your team leader will be there to answer questions.

It is not uncommon to see dramatic healings while praying for people. Some people may fall down under the power of the Holy Spirit (Acts 9:3-4; John 18:4-6). Paralyzed people may be healed and the blind receive their sight (Acts 3:2-10; Matt 12:13; Mark 8:22-25). Let's believe that God will use and work through us powerfully as opportunities to represent Him present themselves (John 14:8-14).

If experiencing these things is new for you, we ask that you observe with an open heart. We have found that team members who go with an open heart have life-changing experiences. Few come home frustrated that they had to observe another expression of evangelical Christianity or be in such a different environment. Experiencing God in a new way often broadens our "lens" and has the potential to draw us into a deeper relationship with Jesus.

Please come prepared to accept others and know that you are fully accepted as you are. You will not be required to participate in any type of ministry in which you are uncomfortable. Please discuss with your team leader any questions or concerns that you might have before and/or after you experience such Christian expression.

Let's expect God to use us in a powerful way!

Logistics

Details

Assignments

- Read and complete Self-Study Three in Team Member Guide
- Prepare your "Personal Story"
- Continue assigned reading material, if applicable
- Study Language Handout, if applicable
- Read Religion Handout, if applicable
- Finish getting your immunizations, if needed
- Send thank you/update to supporters, as needed
- Pray for your team!

Closing Prayer

SELF-STUDY THREE

SELF-STUDY THREE

Introduction

Cross-cultural ministry is extremely dynamic – as you probably realize by now. We hope you are becoming more aware of the different cultures that surround you everyday. You might feel a little bit stretched already! Continue to seek God and depend upon Him – you will never be the same after this trip!

> *Then Peter began to speak: "I now realize how true it is that God does not show favoritism but accepts men from every nation who fear him and do what is right." Acts 10:34-35*

To Complete Before Your Next Team Meeting

Please complete these items for your next meeting. Your team leader will be asking if these items are completed.

- ❑ Read and complete Self-Study Three in Team Member Guide
- ❑ Prepare your "Personal Story"
- ❑ Continue assigned reading material, if applicable
- ❑ Study Language Handout, if applicable
- ❑ Read Religion Handout, if applicable
- ❑ Finish getting your immunizations, if needed
- ❑ Send thank you/update to supporters, as needed
- ❑ Pray for your team!

Social Customs and Sensitivity

Get ready…we will make an impact!

Our very presence on location will have an impact on the people living there. Therefore, it is critical that we do all we can to ensure that our impact is positive. Keep in mind that the nationals will pay <u>very</u> close attention to the team, so please watch what you say and do, so as not to offend them. Think of them before you do anything! Just remember that we, as a team, are representatives of our home church(es), Christians in general, and all future teams.

No matter where you travel, some obvious differences in culture will usually include personal space and punctuality. The nationals may view personal space much differently and may tend to stand or sit much closer or further away than we would. Time frames may be loose or viewed in a much different way than our own. We must be on time as guests in this country, regardless of how "late" we may think our hosts are. Two good sayings to adopt are "be flexible" and "hurry up and wait."

Your team leader may have more information regarding the customs of your specific destination.

Greetings and Hand Gestures

Our hosts may be very warm and outgoing or cold and reserved. In some countries, men and women shake hands when meeting and parting. Men may greet close friends with a hug. Close women friends may greet each other with a kiss on the cheek. Men might also kiss on the cheek. Don't be surprised if you see women walking arm in arm with other women or men with men - it is a sign of close friendship in some cultures.

Typically, the soles of the feet are considered unclean in many places around the world. It would be very rude to show the bottom of your feet or point at someone with your feet, so be careful when crossing your legs!

Some hand gestures in our country can be extremely rude in other countries. Our culture is not nearly as reserved as most of the world when it comes to hand gestures. A motion in our country for someone to come over to you (curling your index finger at someone with your palm up) can be a common call for prostitutes in other cultures! Turning your palm down is a better option. The same miscommunication can apply to winking at someone.

Conversation

The idea of "saving face" is apparent in many cultures around the world, especially in Asia. A national may not say "no" because they do not want to disappoint you – instead, they may tell you what they think you want to hear, rather than what they really think, so they don't "lose face" or offend you. If they are uncomfortable, they may be very vague about the details. Sometimes this is difficult for us "forthright" North Americans to understand – we think "why are they lying?" Keep in mind, they are not "lying," they are trying to save face, not have a negative confrontation, and honor you by not disappointing or offending you.

Good topics of conversations include family, occupation, technology, cultural traditions, or fashion when speaking with women, and of course, spirituality. Topics to avoid: salary, how much you paid for something, government or politics (even if you hear complaints about it), negative remarks about their country, or an individual's ancestors.

Do NOT complain about the conditions, food, habits, hotel standards, noise, smells, etc! Some cultures really like to complain about everything, but don't like people complaining around them. They might also find it extremely rude for people to chew gum in public or eat and drink when they walk. A common mistake by people from the States is to refer to themselves as "Americans" when actually, anybody living in North, Central or South America are also "Americans." To be sensitive, refer to your home as the 'United States' or 'North America.'

Photography

Do NOT photograph airports, military installations, military vehicles, military personnel, or the police without permission. No matter which country you are visiting, you might encounter some sensitivity. Typically other countries are more sensitive than we are in the States for a variety of reasons. Due to heightened security, it is in your best interest to keep your camera tucked away until you arrive at your location! The situation may seem harmless but could turn tenuous very quickly by the simple click of a camera. No picture is worth the safety of the team! Please, don't be selfish and endanger your team.

Whenever taking pictures of people, it is always common courtesy to ask permission first. It is also best to be discreet when taking pictures of indigenous people. Some may object to having their picture taken and some may become angry if you don't offer some local currency in return. Imagine yourself in their place. How would you feel if someone you didn't know came up close and took your picture while you were going about your daily life? Even though most things you encounter will be new and interesting, resist the urge to make a negative impact with overzealous picture taking.

Those "Loud Americans"

Keep in mind that our American culture rewards loud and boisterous behavior, which is usually offensive to other cultures. Many international travelers, mission teams included, have unintentionally embarrassed their hosts and have made a negative impact by simply being "Americans (i.e. loud laughter, joking, talking loudly with each other, etc.)."

Although our outgoing/loud behavior may be a part of our American culture, we must be sensitive when in another country. Keep in mind that our witness can be compromised in those situations. Please confine such behavior to the privacy of your room with other team members or other times when the team is alone. A great rule of thumb is to keep your level of behavior and conversation similar to those around you. If they are quiet and reserved, be quiet and reserved. Just because people might not be able to understand what you are saying verbally, doesn't mean that you aren't communicating a message through tone, volume, and actions.

Gift Giving

The giving of small gifts is common in many countries. If you desire to give someone a small gift, ask your team leader for an appropriate gift suggestion and please be sure to wait until the very last day of the trip to give it, or they may feel obligated to give you a gift in return.

Due to the economy of many lesser-developed countries, please do NOT give money to people or make promises of sending money, clothes, etc. without the direction and approval of your team leader! This is very important. A well-intentioned gift can cause great problems for the international partner. Again, you must submit any intentions to give any type of gift (including money) to the team leader for approval! If this process is not followed, you can do severe damage. The effects of such a well-meaning gesture can be disastrous.

Other tips on gift-giving include: women should be very cautious about giving gifts to male friends so as not to be considered forward. Gifts for the children are always appreciated but again, should only be given after the team leader gives approval. This includes the giving of candy or other small gifts.

Write down any suggestions from your team leader of gifts that would be appropriate for your specific trip/location:

Exercise: Crossing Cultural Boundaries[x]

I have become all things to all men so that by all possible means I might save some. I do all this for the sake of the gospel, that I may share in its blessings. 1 Corinthians 9:22b-23

A person grows up often looking and acting like the cultural background in which he/she was raised. If my cultural background is "square," I turn out to be "square." If it is "round," then I become "round."

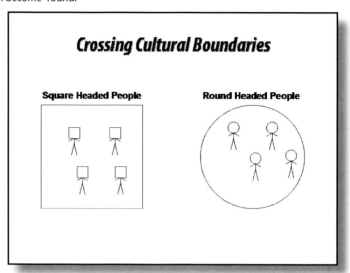

When I leave the safety of my own culture and enter another, I do not leave my cultural "baggage" behind. I take it with me. I may feel like the proverbial "square peg in a round hole."

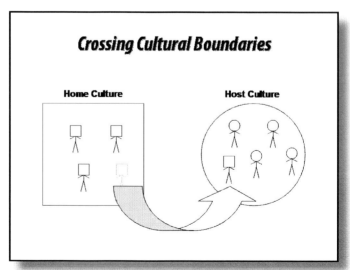

I can adjust and I can fit into the new culture if I put forth an effort. I can adapt to this new culture. I can make the transition effectively and gradually identify more and more with the host culture.

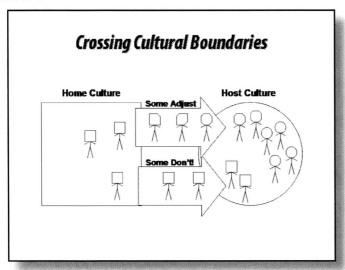

What are some of my "square edges?"

What can I do before leaving to "cut off" those square edges?

What happens when we don't want to or don't try to adjust to the new culture?

How does it affect the ongoing ministry of our host and/or future teams?

Your Personal Story: A Powerful Tool for God

> *"But you will receive power when the Holy Spirit comes on you; and you will be my witnesses in Jerusalem, and in all Judea and Samaria, and to the ends of the earth." Acts 1:8*

Whether we are going on this trip to build a building or preach on the streets, we as Christians are all on the same mission – to be witnesses of Jesus Christ. If you have received Jesus as your Lord and Savior, you have a story to tell. You know the path to a personal relationship with God, your Creator and Savior! You know the cure to the disease of death! And you have the awesome opportunity to tell others about who Jesus is and how to receive this new life.

Think of giving your testimony as you would give a testimony in a court of law. Jesus is on trial – is he really who he says he is? Can he really change lives? You walk by the courtroom as the trial is taking place and hear the people debating this issue. Someone motions for you to come and testify – to share what you have experienced about this Jesus. You take the stand and simply begin sharing how he has changed your life. You know this story because it's yours – you have lived it! The people listening cannot refute your story, because it is *your* testimony — it really happened. And as you share, you become a witness for Jesus!

For some reason, the thought of sharing our faith with others can be a bit scary – but it doesn't have to be that way! Telling people about what God has done for you is not as intimidating as it may seem. As you pray and become aware of the opportunities that God places before you, you'll find it natural to talk about what you love. And with a little preparation and practice, you'll find yourself easily sharing with others a well thought-out story that points people to Jesus. Just think of it…God wants to use you to bring others to eternal life!

Exercise: Writing Your Personal Story

> *"Always be prepared to give an answer to everyone who asks you to give the reason for the hope that you have." 1 Peter 3:15b*

Step #1: Pray

- Praise God for what he has done in your life!

- Pray that God would give you a greater love for him and his people.

- Pray that God would use your personal story to introduce others to Jesus.

- Pray that God would give you clarity of thought and that he would refresh your memory as you prepare.

Step #2: Read Acts 26

Let's get started on preparing your personal story by looking at an example in the life of the apostle Paul. When Paul stood before King Agrippa (Acts 26), he told him simply, logically, and clearly about his life — before salvation, how he met Christ, and what his life was like after his conversion. Paul's story or testimony only takes about 3 to 4 minutes to read aloud in a conversational manner.

Step #3: Sequence your Personal Story

Jot down brief notes in each column below, describing the "BEFORE", "HOW", and "AFTER".

BEFORE	HOW	AFTER
What your life or situation was like before Jesus	How, specifically, you asked Jesus to intervene in your situation	How you have been trans-formed since accepting Christ or since he entered your situation

Tips to keep in mind…

In the BEFORE:

Include both the good and bad aspects of your life.

- Good examples you might include: wanted to excel, desire for education, concern for others, hard working.

- Bad examples you might include: selfish, inferiority complex, get ahead at any cost, temper, greed for finances.

In the HOW:

Use the word "pray" when referring to receiving Christ – this communicates what a person needs to do.

- Good example: "I prayed and repented of my sins. I asked Christ to forgive me and to come into my heart and give me the gift of eternal life."

In the AFTER:

Conclude with two or three personal benefits of becoming a Christian (these may be current benefits). Be specific about how your life has been transformed by Jesus.

- End with something like, "But the greatest benefit is that I know I have eternal life."

- A listener will often remember and comment on the last thing you say. This can give you an open door to present the Gospel.

Step #4: Write Out Your First Draft

Take the notes you jotted down in each column and begin to draft them into paragraphs on the next page. Don't "link" the paragraphs yet, just work on them separately.

Remember to:

- Make it conversational: remember it will be spoken, not read

- Make it personal: use "I" and "me" – not "you"

- Make it real: avoid religious words and phrases

Before:

How:

After:

Step #5: Make the Link

The way you transition from section to section is very important. The link shows your motivation for accepting Christ's intervention in your life and helps the listener understand the end result of life with Christ.

Some suggestions include:

Linking BEFORE and HOW:

- "I realized that I couldn't do it on my own…"
- "I realized that I needed a Savior…"

Linking HOW and AFTER:

- "My life is completely different…"
- "Because of what Jesus has done for me…"
- "Now I know that…"

Step #6: Put It All Together and Adjust as Needed

We suggest that your final version be about 3 minutes long. Some people find it easier to write their testimony out on index cards. Ask a friend to listen to your story and invite their feedback, so it can be a story that is clear and easy to follow.

Different Types of Testimonies

Some of you may not remember exactly when your conversion took place. Or perhaps you don't think your story is as "impacting" as others' experiences. Don't worry! As followers of Christ, we all have stories to share of how Jesus entered into a life situation and changed it around for the good. Testimonies can be prepared on many subjects and tailored for various audiences. When sharing a testimony, be sure to choose only ONE situation or your story will become too vague and hard to follow.

Various types of testimonies that someone can develop through their Christian experience:

Bible study

Answers to prayer

Quiet time

Scripture memory

Victory over sins

Giving

Guidance from God

Marriage and children

Discipling others

Lordship of Christ

Step #7: Become a Natural!

Remember, this is the unique story of what God has done in your life! As you become comfortable sharing it, you will soon be able to share it without notes, just as you would share any other story with a friend. Don't get hung up on it being "perfect." God will use your story to impact lives. Believe it and look for those opportunities!

NOTE: If you will have opportunities for one-on-one evangelism during this trip, your team leader may have you learn how to draw a "Bridge Diagram" like the one in the Appendix, page 158. By learning how to draw this simple diagram and memorizes the key verses, you will be able to clearly convey the way of salvation to someone.

Pray

- Praise God for who He is
- Praise God for what He is going to do through you and the team
- Pray for your team
- Pray for your team leader
- Pray for the people to whom you are going to work/minister

Version: ML Intl-1.1

TEAM MEETING FOUR

TEAM MEETING FOUR

Introduction

Welcome and Prayer

Getting Focused

Bible Verse

Date:	_____
Time:	_____
Location:	_____
Payment Due:	_____

What can we learn from these verses?

How can we apply this to our lives and our mission?

Self-Study Review

Crossing Cultural Boundaries

What are some of our "square edges"?

Why would we want to adjust to the host culture?

Ministry Preparation

Activity: Personal Story

Personal Stories have three parts:

1. BEFORE Jesus was involved in your life/circumstance.

2. HOW Jesus became involved (how you asked).

3. How your life is different AFTER Jesus became involved.

Prayer

- God would open doors of opportunity to share our personal stories.

- We would open our mouths and share our personal stories.

- God would open up the hearts of people to respond to Him.

> *"Always be prepared to give an answer to everyone who asks you to give the reason for the hope that you have."* 1 Peter 3:15b

> *"They overcame him by the blood of the Lamb and by the word of their testimony."* Revelation 12:11a

"I commit to make myself available to God and to respond to opportunities that are presented to me during this trip."

_____

(Your signature)

> *"I can do everything through him who gives me strength."*
> *Philippians 4:13*

Team Building

Activity: Team Building Game

What did I learn about myself?

Logistics

Details

Packing List: See the following pages.

Assignments

- Read and complete Self-Study Four in Team Member Guide
- Pay final payment
- Finish assigned reading material, if applicable
- Start packing!
- Send thank you/update to supporters, as needed
- Pray for your team!

Closing Prayer

What Should I Pack?

Considering the nature of your trip, you may be wearing work clothes (jeans and T-shirts) or nicer clothes if you are teaching leaders and visiting churches. Your team leader can give you specific guidelines on what is appropriate and acceptable. Remember that you will be in a different culture; therefore, we must not assume that what we wear in our country would be appropriate in the country where we will travel. What is considered modest dress in our country can still be offensive in other cultures. Our desire is to build bridges - not to alienate. This means that when it comes to dress, our personal comfort is not always a priority!

Regardless of Your Destination

- **Jeans:** In many developing nations, denim blue jeans are associated with the rebellious youth, so we must be careful to wear them appropriately. If they are allowed on your particular trip, remember that jeans should fit well (not too tight, low, or oversized, like some of the popular styles today) and they should not be torn or frayed.

- **Security:** A money belt, neck wallet, or some sort of hidden pouch is a MUST for your money and passport.

- **Walking Shoes:** Be sure to bring comfortable walking shoes. Assume that you will be walking more than usual. Flip-flops, sandals and even other dressier shoes might not be appropriate.

- **Church Attire:** A good rule of thumb is to dress "business casual" - khaki pants/skirts with shirts/sweaters. If you're speaking, nice attire might be in order - dresses/skirts and jacket/tie.

- **Tight or Revealing Clothing:** Women should not wear any tight clothing, revealing shirts, or short mini-skirts. T-shirts must have sleeves, should cover your mid-section, and should not be low-cut in the neckline.

- **Bathing Suits:** Bathing suits should be one-piece. Even if you are going to Siberia in winter, we suggest packing a bathing suit. You never know where a sauna might appear!

- **Jewelry/Piercing:** Be sensitive to what is appropriate where you are going and keep any jewelry simple. It might not be appropriate for men to wear earrings or members of either sex to have "piercings." Any jewelry beyond the very basic, could be culturally offensive.

- **Advertising:** Always be aware of your witness and be sensitive to what things you might be advertising on your clothing.

- **Travel:** Please dress appropriately when traveling to and from your destination. Pajamas or sweats and other overly casual clothing are not appropriate. Your attire can be comfortable while still being "presentable". Remember, we will make an impression on our hosts whether we are trying to or not.

- **Hot Climates:** Short sleeves and short pant legs aren't always the most cool and comfortable for hot climates. And in some tropical cultures, shorts are definitely not acceptable! Lightweight, fast drying pants, skirts, and long sleeve shirts will keep you from getting sunburned while keeping you cool.

- **Cold Climates:** Layer your clothes. You will stay warmer and will be able to adjust to the fluctuating temperature in your surroundings more easily.

Packing Tips

- Check an internet weather site (such as www.wunderground.com) for the latest forecast for your destination.

- Pack socks, underwear, and T-shirts in Ziploc™ bags. You never know when your bag might get rained on, so it's nice to have dry clothes. You can also push all the "air" out and minimize space.

- If traveling by air, try to put one change of clothes and your toiletries in your carry-on bag, if allowed (be sure to check the latest flight security regulations for your airline). If your checked luggage gets lost, you'll be glad you packed some essentials!

- If using electronic appliances, be sure to bring a <u>voltage converter</u> (if your items are not dual voltage) along with the <u>plug adapters</u>. You can check your owner's manual for which plug adapter to use at your destination; however, we suggest bringing all of your plug adapters, just in case. They do not take up much space and bringing them has proved useful – on more than one trip!

- Don't plan on being able to do laundry while on the trip. If you do get a chance to wash some clothes, great! It will be an added bonus.

- Especially for women: if roommates are known in advance, consider consolidating some of your items (i.e. hair dryer, straightener, curling iron, travel alarm, etc.) to lighten your bags. Also, women should bring feminine hygiene products - even if you don't think you'll need them. They are usually more expensive and difficult to find in other countries.

- Snacks that travel well and will not melt - i.e. trail mix, peanuts, granola bars, raisins and small juice packets are good things to bring along. Bringing a small spoon or fork is helpful. A good missionary ALWAYS has an eating utensil handy! Pack any food in Ziploc™ bags to deter unwanted "visitors" to your luggage.

- Do NOT attempt to carry all the water you might drink on the trip in your luggage!!! Just pack a small water bottle that you can refill. If you will be traveling to a hot climate, a high elevation, and/or involved in physical work, consider bringing "sports drinks" in powdered form to add to your water. This will help your body replenish electrolytes that are sapped from the heat (see also "Food and Water Safety" section, page 83).

- Local Health Department officials recommend using insect repellents with 30% DEET, in order to be effective. In addition, hand sanitizers need at least 60% alcohol content to actually kill germs.

Version: ML Intl-1.1

Suggested Personal Packing List

This list is included as a suggested general packing list and should not be assumed to apply to all travelers. Items shown in italics are not necessarily essential. Your team leader can qualify this list.

TRAVEL DOCUMENTS
- ❑ Passport and visa
- ❑ Airline tickets, if traveling by air
- ❑ Immunization record, if needed
- ❑ Personal emergency health info
- ❑ Medical insurance card
- ❑ Emergency/contact phone numbers
- ❑ Currency
- ❑ Photocopies of tickets, passport, visa
- ❑ "Team Member Guide" with pen or pencil
- ❑ *Credit card*
- ❑ *Guidebooks and maps*
- ❑ *Language phrasebook*

TRAVEL BASICS
- ❑ Bible
- ❑ One personal checked piece of luggage
- ❑ One "ministry/relief supply" checked piece of luggage, if applicable
- ❑ One small backpack or carry-on (with change of clothes)
- ❑ Tags for luggage
- ❑ Locks for luggage, when possible (zip-ties also work well)
- ❑ Travel clothing for specific climate
- ❑ Good walking shoes
- ❑ Light coat or sweater (even for tropical climates)
- ❑ Pajamas (conservative)
- ❑ Visor or brimmed hat
- ❑ Camera
- ❑ Extra batteries
- ❑ Eyeglasses/contacts
- ❑ *Family pictures to share*
- ❑ *Reading material*

GEAR
- ❑ Small flashlight
- ❑ Money belt/neck wallet – a MUST!
- ❑ Travel alarm
- ❑ Earplugs
- ❑ Sunglasses
- ❑ Inexpensive, reliable watch
- ❑ Small, refillable water bottle
- ❑ Voltage converter with plug adapters, if needed

- ❑ *Work gloves, knee pads, dust mask or other work related gear, if needed*
- ❑ *Small gifts for hosts (see Gift Giving section, p. 57)*
- ❑ *Ziploc™ bags*
- ❑ *Snacks, travel utensils, powdered drink mixes (see "Packing Tips" section, p. 73)*

TOILETRIES
- ❑ Personal toiletries: soap, shampoo, deodorant, etc.
- ❑ Toilet paper (1 roll) and/or tissue packets
- ❑ For women: feminine hygiene products
- ❑ Flip-flops for shower, if desired
- ❑ Antibacterial wipes/hand gel (60% alcohol)
- ❑ Sunscreen/lip balm
- ❑ Razor

MEDICATION
- ❑ Aspirin/pain reliever/vitamins, if needed
- ❑ Cold medicine, cough drops/throat lozenges
- ❑ Antacid medicine (such as Pepto-Bismol™ or Tums™)
- ❑ Diarrhea/laxative medicine
- ❑ Insect repellent (30% DEET)/Anti-itch ointment
- ❑ Sunburn relief
- ❑ Motion sickness medication
- ❑ Personal prescriptions/travel meds (in original bottles with original labels)

DON'T GO TO THE AIRPORT WITHOUT...
- ❑ Money belt/neck wallet with all-important documents
- ❑ Carry-on bag
- ❑ One personal bag to check
- ❑ One "ministry/relief supply" bag to check, if applicable
- ❑ A positive attitude!!!

DON'T BRING...
- ❑ Anything that you can't personally carry
- ❑ The kitchen sink
- ❑ A negative attitude!!!

Additional Packing Notes

SELF-STUDY FOUR

SELF-STUDY FOUR

Introduction

Well, the trip is getting closer now! Soon you'll be on your way to your destination with your teammates. Keep the momentum going by focusing on the mission and the great adventure that God has for you and your team.

> *"I can do everything through him who gives me strength."*
> *Philippians 4:13*

To Complete Before Your Next Team Meeting

Please complete these items for your next meeting. Your team leader will be asking if these items are completed.

❑ Read and complete Self-Study Four in Team Member Guide

❑ Pay final payment

❑ Finish assigned reading material, if applicable

❑ Start packing!

❑ Send thank you/update to supporters, as needed

❑ Pray for your team!

Preparing My Heart to Serve

Exercise: Giving Up My Desires

> *"Do nothing out of selfish ambition or vain conceit, but in humility consider others better than yourselves. Each of you should look not only to your own interests, but also to the interests of others."*
> *Philippians 2:3-4*

Due to our sinful nature, we have a tendency as human beings to "look out for number one." This way of thinking permeates our American culture and lifestyle, and as a result, we have a tendency to reflect that attitude without even realizing it.

Take a moment to consider some challenging questions...

What is our motivation for going on this mission trip?

- Do we seek to help or rescue those less "fortunate" than us?
- Do we go to "help them build a better building" or "teach them the Word" – using our "American way" of doing things?
- Do we unknowingly come with expectations of being waited upon – someone getting the materials we will need, the food we will eat, the bed we will sleep in, etc.?
- Or do we come with a mindset of servanthood? Not persuading them to "our way of doing things," but truly serving them in their world?

Read: Mark 10:35-45

What did James and John *really* desire?

What did Jesus give up to serve us?

According to this passage, what does serving require?

How sacrificial am I?   1   2   3   4   5
                           Low   High

What does it mean to "give up my life" for someone else?

What are some practical ways that I could be a servant on this trip?

- To my hosts?

- To my team leader?

- To my fellow team members?

What "choices" am I willing to give up to be a servant on this trip (choice of food, schedule, roommate, etc.)?

Exercise: Why Did Jesus Become a Servant?

Read: Philippians 2:5-11

Does Jesus have a right to be served?

What did he choose to do with his rights?

Why? Did he "hope to gain" glory...or a relationship with us?

According to the Philippians passage, who are we to exemplify?

Our attitude should be the same on this trip. We must choose to give up our perceived "rights" – not just because we are told – but because we desire to build a relationship with our hosts and with those who do not yet know Jesus personally.

What do I need to do before leaving on this trip to prepare my heart to serve?

Health Precautions

Insurance

Taking the necessary precautions when traveling internationally is wise. It is a good idea to check with your personal health insurance carrier to see if they can provide you with coverage when overseas. In addition, your team leader should provide you with more information regarding any short-term medical insurance provided for your team, if applicable.

Immunizations

By this point, you should have received any needed immunizations for your trip. Follow the advice of your medical professional! Remember – you are going to foreign territory. Heed their advice and the advice of your team leader. They are your guides.

Sun Exposure and Insect Concerns

The sun may be much stronger where you are traveling, especially if you will be closer to the equator or at a higher elevation. Even if you are going to a temperate climate, more than likely the nature of your mission will cause you to be outdoors more than usual, so plan on packing sunblock and a hat.

Local Health Department officials recommend using insect repellents with 30% DEET, in order to be effective. Also consider bringing anti-itch ointment for bug-bite relief. Your team leader should let you know if you need mosquito netting.

Sanitary Issues

Bring antiseptic wipes to wipe off toilet seats, toilet paper or small tissue packets (public toilets may not have toilet paper), and a small bottle of hand sanitizer gel to clean your hands frequently. Be aware that hand sanitizers need at least 60% alcohol content to actually kill germs. Women should bring feminine hygiene products - even if you don't think you'll need them. They are usually more expensive and difficult to find in other countries.

Food and Water Safety[xi]

For health considerations, eat well-cooked foods while they are still hot and fruits that can be peeled without contamination. Don't eat shellfish or raw vegetables and avoid road-side stands and street vendors. Eat only thoroughly cooked food or fruits and vegetables you have peeled yourself. Remember: boil it, cook it, peel it, or forget it. Do NOT use ice cubes in anything!

Tap water should NOT be drunk anywhere around the world. There are rare exceptions but it is better to assume that it is NOT safe. Drink only bottled beverages (including water) or beverages made with boiled water. When purchasing bottled water, discreetly check to **make sure that the bottle is sealed before you drink from it** – oftentimes, a street vendor may refill an empty water bottle with tap water and attempt to resell it! Be sure to use bottled water when brushing your teeth as well! Do NOT use ice cubes or eat raw seafood, rare meat, or dairy products. Be aware of raw foods that may have been washed with tap water, such as salads, fresh vegetables, and/or fruit. Ask your team leader if there are any questions on what to eat or drink.

If you are in a remote area where bottled water is unavailable, you might want to have at least one team member pack a water purifier. If this is the case for your team, be sure to bring a purifier rather than just a filter.

It is a good rule of thumb to drink plenty of water when you are in a warm climate. You may also want to bring "sports drinks" in powdered form to add to your water. This will help your body replenish electrolytes that are sapped from the heat. If you are on a work team or at a higher altitude, this should be an even a higher priority. Pack a water bottle that you can easily carry and refill when possible.

Working with Interpreters[xii]

More than likely, you are traveling to a country where English is not the people's first language. So, in order for you to converse with them, you will need to have your words translated into their local language and dialect. Working with interpreters is exciting but can be a little intimidating.

The Basics Include...

- **Show Respect:** When the interpreter is present in your group, never talk negative about their country or culture. Show respect to their way of life even if it is strange or shocking to you. The interpreter may laugh with you, but they are not laughing inside. They may not show it but what you say about their culture can hurt and be offensive to them. They like to hear the good things that you notice about their country and culture.

- **Promises:** Never make promises to the interpreter that you cannot keep!

- **Build Trust:** Have good communication with the interpreter before you go out to minister to others. This will help them not to be nervous and will help them to get use to your voice and vocabulary. You can build trust with them by simply asking them questions.

- **Be Sensitive:** Be sensitive to working too closely with an interpreter of the opposite sex. This is especially true if your mission requires the interpreter to travel with you.

- **Change:** Do not try to convert the interpreter to the American way of life or whatever country you call home.

- **Character:** If the interpreter is not displaying Christian character and attitude, communicate with them and try to help them graciously make the correction. What the people see the interpreter do will reflect on you and future teams. This is a great opportunity for you to disciple someone and encourage them in their faith.

When You Are Preaching or Teaching...

- **Preparation Time:** Make some time with your interpreter to go over material and give them an outline of your message if you have one. Discuss which Bible passages you will be using so the interpreter can review them beforehand.

- **Pray:** Pray with your interpreter before each session.

- **Simplify:** Help the interpreter by keeping sermon and teaching illustrations simple and relative to the local culture. If you have questions regarding this matter, always ask the interpreter before you begin. Keep your language simple, using common words and phrases, without being condescending. Remember that interpreters aren't always "preachers."

- **Repetition:** During a sermon or teaching...if the interpreter does not understand you the first time, just repeat what you said. Say it clearly and loud enough so they can hear you. If they don't understand the second time, say the same thing only in different words.

- **Eye Contact:** Maintain some eye contact with the audience. Do not talk to the interpreter as if he/she is your audience.

- **Timing:** Don't rush your interpreter or you may lose your message. Try to pause for them, if possible.

- **Avoid:** Jokes usually don't go over too well and we advise you to stay away from idioms and analogies. They are confusing, difficult to interpret, and can sometimes be offensive. Inappropriate phrases might include:

    - "If it's too hot, get out of the kitchen"
    - "It's raining cats and dogs"
    - "Flat as a pancake"
    - "Flying by the seat of your pants"
    - "You're in over your head"
    - "We hit a home run"
    - "Coming up roses"
    - "Keep a low profile"
    - "On the same wave length"
    - "On a roll"
    - "Dog and pony show"
    - "I threw my face on my pillow"

Pray

- Praise God for who He is
- Praise God for what He is going to do through you and the team
- Pray for your team
- Pray for your team leader
- Pray for the people to whom you are going to work/minister

Version: ML Intl-1.1

TEAM MEETING FIVE

TEAM MEETING FIVE

Introduction

Welcome and Prayer

Getting Focused

Bible Verse

Date:	_____
Time:	_____
Location:	_____
Payment Due:	_____
	(10 days prior to departure: remainder of trip cost)

What can we learn from these verses?

How can we apply this to our lives and our mission?

Self-Study Review

Preparing My Heart to Serve

Read: John 13:1-17

What is the difference between helping, rescuing, and serving?[xiii]

What are some practical ways that we can be servants on the trip?

Long-Term Impact

Ongoing Relationships

Making Promises
Notes

Ongoing Communication
Notes

Invitations to Visit
Notes

Giving of Money
Notes

Multiplication of Ministry
Notes

Logistics

Details

Departure Meeting Time and Place

Time: _____

Place: _____

Emergency Contact

Name: _____

Number/E-mail: _____

Assignments

- Make 3 copies of your passport and all important documents
- Give your family/loved ones your emergency contact information, for emergencies only
- Contact your prayer team and give an update on how to pray for you and the team
- Send thank you/update to supporters, as needed
- Read and complete Self-Study Five in Team Member Guide
- Finish packing (don't forget your Bible and Team Member Guide)
- Pray for your team!

Closing Prayer

SELF-STUDY FIVE

SELF-STUDY FIVE

Introduction

> *Jesus said, "I am the good shepherd; I know my sheep and my sheep*
> *know me- just as the Father knows me and I know the Father-and I*
> *lay down my life for the sheep. I have other sheep that are not of this*
> *sheep pen. I must bring them also. They too will listen to my voice,*
> *and there shall be one flock and one shepherd. John 10:14-16*

Thank you for working with the "Good Shepherd" to gather His sheep!

To Complete Before Your Departure

Please complete these items before departure. Your team leader will be asking if these items are completed.

❑ Make 3 copies of your passport and all important documents

❑ Give your family/loved ones your emergency contact information, for emergencies only

❑ Contact your prayer team and give an update on how to pray for you and the team

❑ Send thank you/update to supporters, as needed

❑ Read and complete Self-Study Five in Team Member Guide

❑ Finish packing (don't forget your Bible and Team Member Guide)

❑ Pray for your team!

Personal Safety[xiv]

Precautions should always be taken when traveling abroad. In most large urban areas, petty crime is something to be aware of. Travelers should guard against theft of luggage and other belongings, particularly U.S. passports, in international airports and large urban areas. Travelers should use only registered taxis in large cities and should not accept offers of transportation or guide services from individuals seeking clients on the streets. The best preparation is to take all precautions that you would take in a large city like New York or Los Angeles.

- Safety begins when you pack. Leave expensive jewelry, unnecessary credit cards, and anything you would hate to lose at home. Never display large sums of money when paying a bill or shopping.

- Make three photocopies of all valuable documents (passport, visa, airplane tickets, credit cards, driver's license, etc.). Leave one copy at home, pack one copy in your checked luggage and one in your carry-on.

- Do NOT leave valuable items lying around in your room. It is a good idea to lock your suitcases that you leave in your room and to bring extra luggage locks just in case.

- Do NOT expose yourself to dangerous situations, such as darkened streets, alleys, or traveling alone in the city. Never hire a taxi if there is already another passenger in it. Never take a stranger to your hotel room for any reason. Do not open your door to people unknown to you.

- Always travel in groups, even during daylight hours! Do not walk alone, especially late at night or early in the morning. Do NOT shop alone, do not buy too much in one shop, and leave shops well before dark.

- Be aware of your surroundings - especially on public transportation and at tourist sites, food markets, flea markets, and all places where crowds gather. Be very careful with purses, cameras, and other valuables on the streets and in the airports. **Never** take your eyes or hands off your bags!

- ALWAYS keep your passport and money on your person at all times. A trip can turn sour with a lost passport or stolen money. Everyone MUST use a money belt or neck wallet that is secured <u>beneath</u> your clothing for your money, passport and visa. Do NOT trust waist packs or fanny packs with such important documents because pick-pockets have learned that is where the valuables are stored.

- Dress conservatively; a flashy wardrobe or one that is too casual can mark you as a tourist. Foreigners stand out and are a prime target for petty theft in any foreign country, so remember that you are a target for thieves.

NOTE: Although precautions will be taken, occasionally accidents can happen; furthermore, we all know that we live in a different world since 9/11. Individuals should keep in mind that there is a certain amount of risk involved when traveling, just as there is a risk each time one gets behind the wheel of a car. Although it is possible, accidents rarely happen where a team member is injured while participating in a team activity. Please understand that each team member must be fully responsible for knowing their own limitations; <u>no one will be forced to participate in an activity that they feel is out of their physical abilities</u>. Each team member is fully responsible for his/her own personal safety.

Money Issues

Spending Money

Your team leader should provide you with information regarding what is included in your trip cost and what is not.

We suggest that you bring $_____ per person for spending money (depending upon the information outlined by your team leader) and possibly one credit card. When traveling overseas, the bills must be NEW and without marks or tears (bring mostly $20 bills). If you bring a credit card, bring a Visa or MasterCard, as they are the most widely accepted credit cards. However, do not assume that credit cards will be widely accepted in remote locations and PLEASE, GUARD THEM CLOSELY!

In addition, we do not suggest bringing traveler's checks when going to developing countries. We have found that most stores and restaurants do not accept them and changing them can be quite a hassle with additional commission rates. Unfortunately, "traveler's checks" don't seem to be for traveling!

Once on-location, check with your team leader for the exchange rate and best time to exchange money. You probably will not need to have money exchanged right away. Please be understanding, as your team leader will have many other things on their mind other than exchanging money for you. Only use official currency exchange locations. Do NOT exchange money with someone who approaches you on the street! Check an online currency converter before you leave for the latest exchange rate (see our website for a link: www.missiontriptraining.com).

Your team leader should provide you with information regarding payment of group meals. Keep in mind that any "extras" at dinner or room service, laundry, phone calls, faxes, etc. will more than likely be your own responsibility and should be settled at the front desk before the group checks out. Depending upon your particular trip, any sightseeing entrance fees will probably also be at your own expense. Your team leader should provide you with more information.

Remember…keep your money with your passport in a money belt <u>under</u> your clothing!

Tipping

Usually on a mission trip, your team will be traveling together as a group and most of your meals will be eaten together as a group; however, if you find yourself in a "tipping" situation, ask your team leader, translator, or local that you've been working with to assist you.

Shopping

The team MAY have a chance to do some souvenir shopping. We realize that there is an excitement involved with being away from home and wanting to bring back a little "remembrance;" however, please do not lose focus of our mission – witness to the shopkeepers!

Be careful with what you might purchase. Do not purchase any objects of archaeological interest as you will not be able to take them out of the country or you may get in trouble when trying to enter the US and get charged with a fine. Also, some items that appear to be interesting handicrafts may have spiritual meanings or value. We highly suggest NOT purchasing those items. Such items would often include carvings of faces, idols or symbols. Check with your team leader if you have any question.

Oftentimes, you can "haggle" on prices in the markets; however, let them suggest a lower price. Again, please remember we are ultimately there for ministry and not for shopping. Please don't let the opportunity of low prices consume you and cause you to lose focus of your reason for being in the country!

Arrival In-Country

Depending upon the country you are visiting, you will receive immigration cards and customs forms on the last leg of your flight. Fill in the forms as best you can; your team leader should pass around their forms as a sample while in flight. **Do not lose your copy of these forms!** Keep this information with your passport on your person at all times. You will need it when you leave the country.

Upon arrival in country, it will be very important to stay together as a group and listen to your team leader. This experience can often be a little confusing so stay calm, watch your belongings, put your camera away, and wait for instructions. Now is not the time to wander off!

Do not leave your baggage unattended. Do not offer to carry anything for anyone you do not know personally. Do NOT take pictures (reread the "Photography" section, page 56)! Upon arrival, help gather and/or watch baggage. Please do NOT ask your team leader where you can exchange money (see "Spending Money" section, page 97).

Again, it will be critical for everyone to stay together and follow the instructions of the team leader. Stay calm, quiet, and look for ways to assist your team leader.

We're Almost There!

Well, we're almost "on-the-road" - can you believe it? As you have participated in these team meetings and completed your Self-Studies, you have hopefully gained some valuable insight for this trip; and most importantly, you have prepared your heart to serve.

May the Lord bless your willingness to be used by Him. Get ready for a life-changing experience!

Pray

- Praise God for who He is
- Praise God for what He is going to do through you and the team
- Pray for your team
- Pray for your team leader
- Pray for the people to whom you are going to work/minister

ON THE FIELD

ON THE FIELD

Introduction

You have now entered the "mission" portion of this experience! Your days (and nights) will be filled with a busy schedule. You may often be rushing somewhere, just to have to "hurry up and wait." Remember to be flexible! Stay tuned into the Lord, look for ways to serve your team leader and team members, and don't forget to take care of yourself, too - get some sleep when you can!

The following pages will help you process what God is doing in you while you are on the trip. Your leader will be giving you the Bible verses for each day of your devotional. Be sure to complete your daily devotional prior to your team meeting. Then take the time to journal your thoughts and experiences each night. As with most things in life, the more you put into this experience, the more you will get out of it. God bless you as you serve!

Day One

Date: _____

Team Devotional

Bible Verse

What's happening in these verses?

What seems significant to me is...

How can I apply this to my life today?

Daily Journal

Using the space below, spend some time journaling about your day. Answer the question: "What did I see God doing today - in me or around me?" You may want to just draw a quick picture of something significant that happened today.

When you are done, spend some time in prayer - thanking God for who He is and what He is doing on this trip.

Day Two

Date: _____

Team Devotional

Bible Verse

What's happening in these verses?

What seems significant to me is...

How can I apply this to my life today?

Daily Journal

Using the space below, spend some time journaling about your day. Answer the question: "What did I see God doing today - in me or around me?" You may want to just draw a quick picture of something significant that happened today.

When you are done, spend some time in prayer - thanking God for who He is and what He is doing on this trip.

Day Three

Date: _____

Team Devotional

Bible Verse

What's happening in these verses?

What seems significant to me is...

How can I apply this to my life today?

Daily Journal

Using the space below, spend some time journaling about your day. Answer the question: "What did I see God doing today - in me or around me?" You may want to just draw a quick picture of something significant that happened today.

When you are done, spend some time in prayer - thanking God for who He is and what He is doing on this trip.

Day Four

Date: _____

Team Devotional

Bible Verse

What's happening in these verses?

What seems significant to me is...

How can I apply this to my life today?

Daily Journal

Using the space below, spend some time journaling about your day. Answer the question: "What did I see God doing today - in me or around me?" You may want to just draw a quick picture of something significant that happened today.

When you are done, spend some time in prayer - thanking God for who He is and what He is doing on this trip.

Day Five

Date: _____

Team Devotional

Bible Verse

What's happening in these verses?

What seems significant to me is...

How can I apply this to my life today?

Daily Journal

Using the space below, spend some time journaling about your day. Answer the question: "What did I see God doing today - in me or around me?" You may want to just draw a quick picture of something significant that happened today.

When you are done, spend some time in prayer - thanking God for who He is and what He is doing on this trip.

Day Six

Date: _____

Team Devotional

Bible Verse

What's happening in these verses?

What seems significant to me is...

How can I apply this to my life today?

Daily Journal

Using the space below, spend some time journaling about your day. Answer the question: "What did I see God doing today - in me or around me?" You may want to just draw a quick picture of something significant that happened today.

When you are done, spend some time in prayer - thanking God for who He is and what He is doing on this trip.

Day Seven

Date: _____

Team Devotional

Bible Verse

What's happening in these verses?

What seems significant to me is...

How can I apply this to my life today?

Daily Journal

Using the space below, spend some time journaling about your day. Answer the question: "What did I see God doing today - in me or around me?" You may want to just draw a quick picture of something significant that happened today.

When you are done, spend some time in prayer - thanking God for who He is and what He is doing on this trip.

Day Eight

Date: _____

Team Devotional

Bible Verse

What's happening in these verses?

What seems significant to me is...

How can I apply this to my life today?

Daily Journal

Using the space below, spend some time journaling about your day. Answer the question: "What did I see God doing today - in me or around me?" You may want to just draw a quick picture of something significant that happened today.

When you are done, spend some time in prayer - thanking God for who He is and what He is doing on this trip.

Day Nine

Date: _____

Team Devotional

Bible Verse

What's happening in these verses?

What seems significant to me is...

How can I apply this to my life today?

Daily Journal

Using the space below, spend some time journaling about your day. Answer the question: "What did I see God doing today - in me or around me?" You may want to just draw a quick picture of something significant that happened today.

When you are done, spend some time in prayer - thanking God for who He is and what He is doing on this trip.

Day Ten

Date: _____

Team Devotional

Bible Verse

What's happening in these verses?

What seems significant to me is...

How can I apply this to my life today?

Daily Journal

Using the space below, spend some time journaling about your day. Answer the question: "What did I see God doing today - in me or around me?" You may want to just draw a quick picture of something significant that happened today.

When you are done, spend some time in prayer - thanking God for who He is and what He is doing on this trip.

Day Eleven

Date: _____

Team Devotional

Bible Verse

What's happening in these verses?

What seems significant to me is...

How can I apply this to my life today?

Daily Journal

Using the space below, spend some time journaling about your day. Answer the question: "What did I see God doing today - in me or around me?" You may want to just draw a quick picture of something significant that happened today.

When you are done, spend some time in prayer - thanking God for who He is and what He is doing on this trip.

Day Twelve

Date: _____

Team Devotional

Bible Verse

What's happening in these verses?

What seems significant to me is...

How can I apply this to my life today?

Daily Journal

Using the space below, spend some time journaling about your day. Answer the question: "What did I see God doing today - in me or around me?" You may want to just draw a quick picture of something significant that happened today.

When you are done, spend some time in prayer - thanking God for who He is and what He is doing on this trip.

Day Thirteen

Date: _____

Team Devotional

Bible Verse

What's happening in these verses?

What seems significant to me is...

How can I apply this to my life today?

Daily Journal

Using the space below, spend some time journaling about your day. Answer the question: "What did I see God doing today - in me or around me?" You may want to just draw a quick picture of something significant that happened today.

When you are done, spend some time in prayer - thanking God for who He is and what He is doing on this trip.

Day Fourteen

Date: _____

Team Devotional

Bible Verse

What's happening in these verses?

What seems significant to me is...

How can I apply this to my life today?

Daily Journal

Using the space below, spend some time journaling about your day. Answer the question: "What did I see God doing today - in me or around me?" You may want to just draw a quick picture of something significant that happened today.

When you are done, spend some time in prayer - thanking God for who He is and what He is doing on this trip.

Blank pages are available at the back of your Team Member Guide, if you need more space.

DEBRIEF AND RE-ENTRY MEETING

DEBRIEF AND RE-ENTRY MEETING

Introduction

Welcome and Prayer

Getting Focused

Bible Verse

What can we learn from these verses?

How can we apply this to our lives and our mission?

Trip Debrief

Thoughts and Emotions

Debriefing and re-entry is a process, not a one-time activity. You have experienced something incredible and "beyond the norm" for most people. Taking the time NOW to apply this unique event is essential to receiving the greatest impact from your trip. You are now entering the "post-trip" portion of this experience. The experience is not over when you arrive back in your hometown. Like a plant, you were uprooted from your life at home to go on this trip. Now it's time to "uproot" again and return back home. A major part of the experience is just beginning. This is where it can get REALLY exciting for you personally!

More than likely, there are a variety of thoughts and emotions going through your mind at this point on the trip. You've met new friends, you've experienced new things, you've seen God use you to affect other people's lives, and you've come together as a team with people you really didn't know well before you left. And at the same time, you are probably craving that pizza or hamburger that you can't WAIT to eat! You can't wait to sleep in your own bed…with your own pillow. And you've started to envision seeing your loved ones again.

Memorable Moments

What moments will you remember most?

What impacted you the most?

What did you experience that was different on this trip?

How are <u>you</u> different?

Activity: Paper Pass[xv]

Name: _____

Activity: The Soil of our Heart

Listen: Matthew 13:1-23

Notes:

"God, I believe by faith, that _____ people back home will be impacted through me as a result of this trip."

Opportunity and Responsibility

We have an awesome opportunity and responsibility to share with others what we saw and experienced. Our story can greatly affect other people! We have an opportunity to encourage people in their faith, testify to what God has done, and ENCOURAGE people to live a life for God; to be used by Him in their own neighborhood and to the ends of the earth. People are expecting to hear from you about the trip. Look for opportunities and don't shy away from giving praise to God!

- Send follow-up correspondence to those that prayed and gave resources.
- Share with family members.
- Share with friends.
- Look for opportunities to share at school and work.
- Expect God to open doors for you to tell people about this trip and how it changed your life!

Re-Entry

The Reality of Going Home

Notes:

Typical responses:

- Sadness and guilt at the realization of all that we have and what most of the world doesn't have.

- Anger or frustration with other citizens at home who don't realize we have so much while others – even within our own country – have so little.

- Tension with other Christians that don't think "going to the ends of the earth" is such a big deal.

- Joy and gladness due to your deepening realization of who God is and how He wants to use you.

- Gratitude for your family, freedom to worship, and resources available to you.

- Appreciation for other people.

Activity: Re-Entry Imagery

Think of three main things that happened on the trip that really stand out to you. It can be very personal or an event that happened to the whole team. It can be something that God whispered to your heart during a bus ride or what it felt like when you saw masses of people come to know Christ during a church service.

Take a couple of minutes and write down three things:

1. _____

2. _____

3. _____

Now, of those three experiences, choose the one that is the MOST impacting to you. In the space provided, write out the details of that experience.

Circle the main points of your story.

Then think through how you will communicate those main points in just a couple of minutes.

Think of this as your "IMPACT" Story. If you had just a minute or two, how would you share about your trip?

My Impact Story

Life Application

"In response to who God is and what He has done in my life during this trip, I commit to:

_____

_____

_____."

There is no "right" answer! In the past, some team members have committed to:

- Pray daily for the host ministry.
- Pray for the host country/region and the advancement of the Gospel.
- Pray for the missions ministry of their local church.
- Pray more in general.
- Give to the host ministry.
- Give to future teams and team members.
- Give more of their lives and agenda over to God.
- Go and share what God has done in them.
- Go and recruit other team members.
- Go on a future trip or for an extended period.
- Go to neighbors, co-workers, people in the community, and/or family members that don't know Christ.

What is your next step?

Logistics

Celebration Party

Date: _____

    (Within 2 weeks of return home)

Time: _____

Location:_____

I will invite _____ to the Celebration Party.

Going Home

Long-Term Impact

Ongoing Relationships

- **Making Promises:** Saying good-bye to your new friends will be VERY emotional! Do NOT make promises to anyone as you say your good-byes – including promises to write, e-mail, or send photos. Circumstances beyond your control may restrict the fulfillment of your promise, which can crush the hearts of your new friends. Unfulfilled promises can also affect future relations with other teams. Unfortunately, we've seen it happen too many times. Please be sensitive and try to remember the "big picture."

- **Ongoing Communication:** don't share your personal information.

- **Invitations to Visit:** discuss with your team leader and wait at least 6 months before inviting someone.

- **Giving of Money:** always ask the team leader! Any donations to the host ministry should be directed to your team leader. In addition, team members should not make financial promises of any nature without the consultation of the team leader.

Evaluations

Evaluations are located in the back of your Team Member Guide.

Complete, tear out, and return to team leader by: _____

Last Minute Details

- Passports, plane tickets, and immigration cards (check for them NOW, before we get to the airport!)

- Foreign currency exchange

- Departure schedule

Closing Prayer

"The harvest is plentiful but the workers are few. Ask the Lord of
the harvest, therefore, to send out workers into his harvest field."
Matthew 9:37-38

Team Member Evaluation

We strive for excellence in missions and constantly seek to improve the effectiveness of short-term ministry. We want short-term missions to be a life-changing discipleship experience that will turn mission travelers into life-long harvest workers. Your input plays a valuable role in helping us further this goal. Thank you for taking the time to answer these questions thoroughly.

Your Involvement

Trip Name and Dates: _____

How did you find out about this trip and what caused you to join this team?

Would you go again on a short-term trip?　　　　❑ Yes　　❑ No

Why or why not?

If Yes:

- When?
- Where?
- What type of trip?

Please rate the following areas using the scale provided.

Preparation, Organization, and Leadership

Training and preparation for travel and ministry.
　　　　1　　2　　3　　4　　5
　　　　Low　　　　　　　High

Comments:

Organization of the trip.
　　　　1　　2　　3　　4　　5
　　　　Low　　　　　　　High

Comments:

Knowledge and effectiveness of the leader.
　　　　1　　2　　3　　4　　5
　　　　Low　　　　　　　High

Comments:

Personal Impact

My spiritual growth.	1	2	3	4	5
	Low				High

Comments:

My personal effort on the team.	1	2	3	4	5
	Low				High

Comments:

My overall personal experience.	1	2	3	4	5
	Low				High

Comments:

The affect of this experience to my daily life.	1	2	3	4	5
	Low				High

Comments:

Ministry/Work Impact

The impact of our team's ministry/work.	1	2	3	4	5
	Low				High

Comments:

Suggestions for Greater Impact

These short-term mission teams could have an even greater impact if they would...

When you are finished, tear out and hand in to your team leader.

Thank you for your feedback!

APPENDIX

Support Raising Packet

Introduction

Welcome!

As followers of Christ we are commissioned to be continually inviting people into a deeper relationship with Him. Giving others opportunity to be used by God is a tremendous blessing! Be encouraged, God wants people to be praying for you on this trip, as well as supporting you through their financial gifts!

Why Raise Support?

Every team member/family needs support from the wider body of Christ. We need the encouragement that comes from knowing friends and family members are behind us. We need the strength and protection that comes through prayer. And we need the Holy Spirit going before us to prepare hearts for the Gospel message.

Therefore, we highly suggest that all team members send out support letters. A support letter asks for the involvement of people in prayer and/or financial support. We want each team member/family to develop a support team. Not only will this further our mission, but it will involve many more people in it, strengthening and growing the church in its passion for God's mission.

> *He said to them, "Go into all the world and preach the good news to all creation." Mark 16:15*

Part of your spiritual preparation for this trip is raising your support. You have the desire to go, but may not have the personal finances to make it possible. We have good news! God wants to provide!

> *"God's work, done God's way, will never lack God's supply."*
> *Hudson Taylor, Missionary to China*
>
> *"...the worker is worth his keep." (see Matthew 10:5-10)*
>
> *Jesus and the twelve were supported by others (see Luke 8:1-3)*
>
> *Paul was supported on his mission trips by others (see Romans 15:20-24)*

Keys to Support Raising

Many team members start out thinking of support raising as "begging". Nothing could be further from the truth. Being a follower of Christ, we should always be looking for opportunities to get people involved in God's work. This is not a "necessary evil;" rather, **this is an opportunity** to be used by God to draw people to Himself! Now that's exciting! Literally, think of support raising as an opportunity to share with others what God is doing and allow them to get involved. You'll be shocked by how many people want to support God's work through you. God's plan for this trip is much larger than our own.

Prayer Support

Having the prayer support of others is critical for the success of this mission. Do not make prayer support secondary to financial support.

The recruitment of a prayer support team is mandatory. All team members must obtain commitments for consistent and persistent prayer support. We suggest having **5-10 people** committed to pray for you.

Contact these people in person, by phone, e-mail, or by letter. Make sure they know that you want them to pray for you daily while on the trip and to also be praying for you before and after the trip as the Holy Spirit leads them.

Before you leave on the trip, make sure to provide your prayer support team with a short list of "prayer points" so they can pray specifically and personally for you.

Financial Support

OK, let's admit it – most people don't enjoy raising financial support. It's scary, right? We often feel "strange" asking other people for money. Why is this?

Your biggest obstacle when it comes to raising financial support is not the cost of the trip or the uncertainty of whether or not people will give; the biggest obstacle is probably YOU! <u>We</u> **are the biggest barriers.**

We focus too much on ourselves - wondering what others are going to think of us when we share the need. Will they question our motives, the mission, or will they think that we are poor or too cheap?

KEY: Focus on God rather than yourself! Give God the opportunity to prove Himself able by trusting in Him and faithfully doing your part.

Our focus needs to be on God and Him alone. If we keep our eyes on Him, we will not "sink below the waves" as Peter did when he walked on the water toward Jesus (Matthew 14:25-33). When we share the opportunity to get involved, we should stress how incredible it is to be partnering with God in what He is doing around the world! Let's get ourselves out of the way and allow people to see God in our lives and efforts in this mission.

Even if you can fund your trip yourself, **we highly suggest that all team members consider raising financial support.** There are always supplies to purchase and some team members might need some additional financial help. Also, the national partner might have a special project that could use some funds as well.

There are many "fundraising" ideas, but the one tool that seems to be the most effective is the **sending of personal letters.** It is highly personal and allows for the communication of your passion to "Go" as well as the opportunity for people to respond.

"You did not choose me, but I chose you and appointed you to go and bear fruit-fruit that will last. Then the Father will give you whatever you ask in my name." John 15:16

"And pray for us, too, that God may open a door for our message, so that we may proclaim the mystery of Christ, for which I am in chains. Pray that I may proclaim it clearly, as I should." Colossians 4:3-4

Policy

All checks/donations must be made out to the church or non-profit organization in order for the donor to receive a tax credit. Your name should NOT appear on the check; rather, there should be a note enclosed identifying the individual and the trip for which the donation is intended.

- All donations are non-refundable.

- Responding to the donors is solely your responsibility. You'll want to thank them anyway!

KEY: *A key to raising financial support is to start early - with a list of about 50 people! Four to five months before departure is NOT too early. God wants to provide but He needs you to partner with Him.*

Steps to Support Raising

Step One: Commit your Work to the Lord

- Begin with prayer. Stop right now and commit yourself to God.

> *"If you believe, you will receive whatever you ask for in prayer."*
> *Matthew 21:22*

- Admit your need for total dependence upon Him.

> *"Trust in the LORD with all your heart and lean not on your own understanding." Proverbs 3:5*

- Ask God to give you a **teachable heart** as you prepare for the trip and allow you to learn more about Him during this process of raising support. Don't miss this HUGE opportunity to draw closer to God!

- Pray that God would build your faith.

Step Two: Identify Contacts

If you are having difficulty coming up with names for your mailing list, use the brainstorming pages to help you. Categories of friends and acquaintances are listed on the following pages to stimulate your thinking and to help you organize your names. Many of your acquaintances might fall under several categories. However, list each one only once. Don't feel like you need to fill every slot in every category. Remember: It will be easier to scratch names from your list than to add names.

- **Resist the urge to "blanket" your church with letters**. Choose only those you <u>personally</u> know well. Be creative and look outside the church to expand God's influence in the lives of people. Remember, there is outreach potential here!

- **No address, no problem!** Even if you don't have the address, put the name down anyway. You can get others to help you track down an address. The person that you can't reach may be the one who needs the ministry you can give!

- **Communicate your trip with non-Christians**. That's right. Non-Christians will most likely "admire" what you are going to do and it will peak their interest. Make sure that unbelievers are on your mailing list. Even if they don't support you financially, ask them if you can share the experience with them when you get home. You'll find that 99% of people will want to hear about your trip.

- **Don't judge** whether people have the ability to give or not. This can be very difficult. Remember, you are only giving them an opportunity to get involved. Let them decide if they can or should give.

- **Pray and obey God's leading**. You might be surprised to whom God is leading you to send letters. Follow that leading. Remember that God's plan for this trip is far larger than ours. He might use your letter to impact somebody's life that you wouldn't expect.

Step Three: Type Your Letter

Once you have collected your names, you can begin to write your letter. A sample letter has been enclosed to guide you. Keep your letter to one page and include these aspects in your letter.

1. How God is working in your life currently

2. The opportunity you have to serve God as a part of this team

3. How you expect God to work in your own life

4. The cost of the trip

5. How soon you need to raise support

6. Specifically how the supporter can help you reach your goals and impact people

Once opened, your letter has about 20 seconds to capture the reader's attention. Therefore, keep these things in mind:

- **Be Personal:** Write a personalized hand-written note on all letters. This note will stand out and is often read first. Personally sign each letter and include a photo of yourself.

- **Be Brief:** People get a lot of mail today. Avoid long words and sentences. Write in conversational language. Keep the letter to one page in length.

- **Be Specific:** Tell them how they can be involved in this experience (prayer and financial support) and give them some financial increments to chose from (example: $100, $50, $25).

- **Be Clear:** Ask someone else to read your letter and give you input.

- **Be Accurate:** Check your spelling. Be sure that your trip details are accurate and be clear about how they can respond.

Step Four: Assemble Your Packets

Once your letter is written, duplicate it as many times as necessary. Try to get good, clean copies. After writing any personal notes on the letters, you're ready to prepare your packet. This packet should include:

1. Letter

2. Response form with your name on it

3. Self addressed, stamped envelope with your address

> *KEY: Providing people with a convenient way to respond is important. Include this statement in your letter: "We have included two items in this packet to help you with this." This will increase the possibility that they will respond.*

You will want the responses to come back to you so you can know who has responded and who hasn't. You'll want to send a "thank you" note to those that responded right away!

Response Form. A page of sample response forms is included. You may use it to design your own; otherwise, you have permission to photocopy the response form page and cut them out. Write your name in the "Team Member I'm Supporting" blank.

> *KEY: Your letters need to be mailed at least 4 months prior to departure in order to allow people to respond and meet payment due dates.*

Step Five: Follow-Up

This can be a critical step in gaining support. Some people will want to support you but they may have lost your letter in the piles of other mail they receive or they may have just set the letter aside. They may need personal contact such as a phone call, e-mail, or a visit to see if they received your letter and/or if they have any questions. Use this opportunity to update them with details about the trip and the preparation of the team.

Step Six: Respond to Supporters

It is crucial that people know you <u>appreciate</u> their support and don't take their prayers or financial gifts for granted. When someone indicates a willingness to support you financially or by prayer, you MUST send a thank-you note. This will allow them to know you received their support and that you appreciate their sacrifice!

Failure to complete this step can turn people away from missions and could possibly stop them from ever wanting to be involved again. You are reaping the benefit of their sacrifice, please take this responsibility seriously!

A form has been provided on the following pages to help you track who you've sent a letter to and if they have replied.

After the trip, report back to these supporters with photos and personal stories. Invite them to the Celebration Party and **let them know that they are part of the team!**

Brainstorming Pages

Friends From Other Churches in Your Area (not your home church)

1.	9.	17.
2.	10.	18.
3.	11.	19.
4.	12.	20.
5.	13.	21.
6.	14.	22.
7.	15.	23.
8.	16.	24.

Co-Workers/Business Associates

1.	6.	11.
2.	7.	12.
3.	8.	13.
4.	9.	14.
5.	10.	15.

Neighbors

1.	6.	11.
2.	7.	12.
3.	8.	13.
4.	9.	14.
5.	10.	15.

Friends From College or Military Days

1.	6.	11.
2.	7.	12.
3.	8.	13.
4.	9.	14.
5.	10.	15.

Friends From Former Residences, Churches, Jobs

1.	13.	25.
2.	14.	26.
3.	15.	27.
4.	16.	28.
5.	17.	29.
6.	18.	30.
7.	19.	31.
8.	20.	32.
9.	21.	33.
10.	22.	34.
11.	23.	35.
12.	24.	36.

Friends From Other Cities

1.	9.	17.
2.	10.	18.
3.	11.	19.
4.	12.	20.
5.	13.	21.
6.	14.	22.
7.	15.	23.
8.	16.	24.

Relatives and Family Friends

1.	6.	11.
2.	7.	12.
3.	8.	13.
4.	9.	14.
5.	10.	15.

Friends From Athletic/Social/Service Organizations

1.	6.	11.
2.	7.	12.
3.	8.	13.
4.	9.	14.
5.	10.	15.

Friends From "Back Home" (where you grew up)

1.	6.	11.
2.	7.	12.
3.	8.	13.
4.	9.	14.
5.	10.	15.

People You've Ministered To (Sunday School, Bible Studies, etc.)

1.	6.	11.
2.	7.	12.
3.	8.	13.
4.	9.	14.
5.	10.	15.

Friends From Church (try to work <u>outside</u> your church first!)

1.	13.	25.
2.	14.	26.
3.	15.	27.
4.	16.	28.
5.	17.	29.
6.	18.	30.
7.	19.	31.
8.	20.	32.
9.	21.	33.
10.	22.	34.
11.	23.	35.
12.	24.	36.

You might also want to try to think of people in the following career fields:

Accountants	Contractors	Entrepreneurs	Landscaping
Athletes	Dentists	Executives	Large Companies
Auto Industry	Doctors	Farming	Lawyers
Banking	Electricians	Government	Nurses
Chiropractors	Engineers	Insurance	Optometrists
Pastors	Pharmacists	Pilots	Printers
Real Estate	Retailers	Service Industries	Small Businesses
Teachers			

You won't necessarily send a support letter to all these people, but they form your pool of contacts. Spend time in prayer, asking God to lead you to send letters to the right people.

Sample Support Raising Letter

John,

I hope you are having a GREAT summer! You are an important person in my life so I want to share with you an exciting opportunity that I am going to be a part of this upcoming summer.

My relationship with Jesus is growing and I've chosen to follow His leading to go on a short-term mission trip. I am so excited to step out in faith and serve God in this adventure! There is an incredible opportunity to go with a team from my church to the country of Bangladesh.

Imagine 143 million people in a land area the size of Arkansas! That's Bangladesh. Approximately 87% of the people adhere to the Muslim faith with a small 3% of the population bravely declaring Jesus as their Savior. My church is connected with an organization there that is run by nationals and is doing incredible humanitarian work. They also share the reality of a personal relationship with Jesus through their work and send evangelists into rural villages.

On this trip, our team will be leading a day camp with crafts, games, and Bible teaching for approximately 1,100 underprivileged and orphaned children! Yes, 1,100! We will also be doing some evangelism in predominately Muslim villages. The opportunities for God to impact the lives of people are endless. Recently there has been some great success in leading Muslims to Christ through this type of ministry. I'm so excited!

I need 10 prayer partners that would begin praying now for the success of this missionary trip. I would like to offer you the opportunity to join me in praying for this trip. Prayer is essential for the team's success and safety.

Also, I would like to ask you to partner with me financially in order to make this journey. The cost is ($) and I would ask you to prayerfully consider sending me to help these people. If (#) of my friends and family will give ($) each, I will be able to serve as God's tool in this remote region. Would you pray about being one of my supporters and respond by mailing the attached form by (date)?

The trip leaves (date), so I do need to hear back from you as soon as possible. Please respond as the Lord leads you by using the attached form and envelope.

Thanks, John! I'll contact you again soon to update you about the team's preparation.

Have an awesome day!

(Signed with personal note)

Sample Response Form

You may use this page to design your own response form; otherwise, you have permission to photocopy this response form page and cut them out. Write your name in the "Team Member I'm Supporting" blank.

Missions Support Response Form

My Name: _____

Team Member I'm Supporting: _____

Country and Date of Trip: _____

❑ I would like to be a part of your prayer support team. Please send me your requests.

❑ I would like to be a part of your financial support team by giving $_____.

- Please make checks payable to _____ (Team Member's Church).
- Write _____ (Trip Name and Dates) in the memo field.
- **DO NOT put name of person being sponsored on the check.**

Missions Support Response Form

My Name: _____

Team Member I'm Supporting: _____

Country and Date of Trip: _____

❑ I would like to be a part of your prayer support team. Please send me your requests.

❑ I would like to be a part of your financial support team by giving $_____.

- Please make checks payable to _____ (Team Member's Church).
- Write _____ (Trip Name and Dates) in the memo field.
- **DO NOT put name of person being sponsored on the check.**

Missions Support Response Form

My Name: _____

Team Member I'm Supporting: _____

Country and Date of Trip: _____

❑ I would like to be a part of your prayer support team. Please send me your requests.

❑ I would like to be a part of your financial support team by giving $_____.

- Please make checks payable to _____ (Team Member's Church).
- Write _____ (Trip Name and Dates) in the memo field.
- **DO NOT put name of person being sponsored on the check.**

Supporter Tracking Sheet

You have permission to photocopy these two pages for this mission trip, if you need more space.

#	Name	Address	City, State, Zip
1			
2			
3			
4			
5			
6			
7			
8			
9			
10			
11			
12			
13			
14			
15			
16			
17			
18			
19			
20			
21			
22			
23			
24			
25			

Comments:

Response	Amount	Sent Thank You	Prayer Team

Comments:

Bridge Diagram

Drawing out a diagram, such as the one below, is an excellent way to share the Gospel visually. You can draw it on a piece of scrap paper (or even a napkin) and give it to the person so they can take it with them to study later. Memorize the corresponding verses and you will be equipped to share the Gospel message wherever you go!

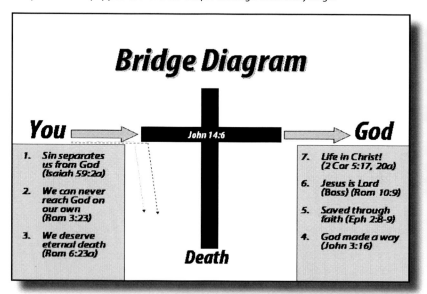

1. Write "You" on the left side of the paper and "God" on the right. Explain that our sin separates us from a holy God and draw the two "cliffs" on either side, with "Death" at the bottom. Quote/read Isaiah 59:2a.

   But your iniquities have separated you from your God; Isaiah 59:2a

2. Explain how we may try to reach God, but we can never reach Him on our own because we are sinful. Draw arrows that don't make it to God and quickly fall down towards death (i.e. good works, go to church, be a good person, help the needy, etc.). These good things will not get us into heaven [NOTE: this is the major difference that sets Christianity apart from all other religions]. Quote/read Romans 3:23.

   For all have sinned and fall short of the glory of God, Romans 3:23

3. Explain how our sin (no matter how insignificant we may think it is) deserves punishment (death) because God is perfect, holy, and just and He must punish sin. Quote/read Romans 6:23a. Without a solution, we will be separated from God for eternity.

   For the wages of sin is death, Romans 6:23a

4. Explain that there is good news - God made a way for us to escape death and have life with Him. He sent His own son, Jesus, to die in our place for our sins. Draw a cross to connect the two sides. Quote/read John 3:16 and John 14:6.

> *For God so loved the world that he gave his one and only Son, that whoever believes in him shall not perish but have eternal life. John 3:16*
>
> *Jesus answered, "I am the way and the truth and the life. No one comes to the Father except through me." John 14:6*

5. Explain that just knowing about this good news is not enough to save us. We must realize our hopeless condition (that we are headed towards death) and be willing to receive this free gift of eternal life in Christ. We must <u>believe</u> in faith that Jesus saves us and we must <u>receive</u> His free gift (we must walk across the bridge). Quote/read Ephesians 2:8-9.

> *For it is by grace you have been saved, through faith-and this not from yourselves, it is the gift of God- not by works, so that no one can boast. Ephesians 2:8-9*

6. Quote/read Romans 10:9. Ask them if they are ready to cross over from death to life by receiving Jesus as their Savior and Lord ("Boss"- meaning He is in control). Pray with them, if they indicate they are ready.

> *That if you confess with your mouth, "Jesus is Lord," and believe in your heart that God raised him from the dead, you will be saved. Romans 10:9*

7. Explain that God's Spirit now lives inside them and will give them the power to be transformed into a new creature. Explain that God wants to use them to impact other people with this same good news. Quote/read 2 Corinthians 5:17, 20a.

> *Therefore, if anyone is in Christ, he is a new creation; the old has gone, the new has come! We are therefore Christ's ambassadors, as though God were making his appeal through us. 2 Corinthians 5:17, 20a*

Recommended Reading List

Some of our favorite books on missions include:

- *Bruchko* by Bruce Olson
- *Cross-Cultural Connections* by Duane Elmer
- *Eternity in Their Hearts* by Don Richardson
- *Foreign to Familiar* by Sarah A. Lanier
- *Let the Nations be Glad!* by John Piper
- *Peace Child* by Don Richardson
- *Six Dangerous Questions to Transform Your View of the World* by Paul Borthwick

We also recommend attending the **Urbana Conference**, held every 3 years (www.urbana.org).

About the Authors

Eric and Carol Hanson have been involved in short-term missions for over ten years. Shortly after their first mission trip to Nigeria in 1995, they joined Missions International in Nashville, TN, where they learned how to deploy short-term mission teams. They have been privileged to work with many denominations within North America, as well as other nations. They have taken countless teams to over 20 countries – ministering through street evangelism, church planting, leadership training, children's ministry, worship conferences, orphanage ministry, construction, and medical clinics. They have both spoken at the National Short-Term Missions Conference, teaching on team building and training national leaders.

Previously, Eric directed the missions ministry for their church in Nashville, TN and now serves as the International Impact Director for Christ Community Church, outside Chicago, IL. With her additional background in training and development, Carol is thrilled to apply her experience to train short-term mission teams. In addition to this discipleship training curriculum, they have also written self-study materials called "Get Ready! Guides," which can be customized for an organization, church, or particular trip. Eric and Carol have a passion for the nations and a desire to see team members discipled…as they go to make disciples. They reside in Sycamore, IL where they are raising their two children.

For more information on training materials for your short-term mission teams, contact Eric and Carol Hanson at Mission Excell: info@missiontriptraining.com.

Please visit our website: www.missiontriptraining.com

Endnotes

i   Some questions adapted from *Vacations With a Purpose* by Chris Eaton and Kim Hurst; Cook Ministry Resources (Colorado Springs: 1996) 96-99.

ii   Ibid. 103-105.

iii   Excerpts from old *Team Member Prep Kits*, Missions International (Nashville, TN). www.missions.com

iv   Adapted version of a public domain handout received from Dr. Duane Elmer. In his book, *Cross-Cultural Connections*, he sources: "Faculty of Missionary Internship, 'The Cultural Adjustment Map,' Farmington, Mich.: Missionary Internship, 1975. This classroom presentation is freely shared with anyone who wants to use it as public domain."

v   Excerpts from old *Team Member Prep Kits*, Missions International (Nashville, TN). www.missions.com

vi   Bryant L. Myers, *Exploring World Mission: Context & Challenges*; World Vision International (Monrovia: 2003) 52

vii   Ibid. 54

viii   Biblesoft's *New Exhaustive Strong's Numbers and Concordance with Expanded Greek-Hebrew Dictionary*. Copyright © 1994, 2003 Biblesoft, Inc. and International Bible Translators, Inc.

ix   Wayne Grudem, *Bible Doctrine, Essential Teachings of the Christian Faith* (Grand Rapids: 1989) 396 footnotes

x   Adapted version of a public domain handout received from Dr. Duane Elmer. In his book, *Cross-Cultural Connections*, he sources: "Dwight Gradin, 'Square Heads, Round Heads' (Farmington, Mich.: Missionary Internship, 1973). He has freely shared the diagram in his class presentations as public domain."

xi   Adapted from U.S. Department of State website. http://www.state.gov

xii   Jim Harper, from conversations with Jim on past short-term trips (Vladivostok: 1998)

xiii   Adapted from *Vacations With a Purpose* by Chris Eaton and Kim Hurst; Cook Ministry Resources (Colorado Springs: 1996) 113

xiv   Excerpts taken from U.S. Department of State website. http://www.state.gov (updated November 2005)

xv   Adapted from *The Essential Guide to the Short-Term Mission Trip* by David C. Forward; Moody Press (Chicago: 1998) 176-177.

Version: ML Intl-1.1

GROUP

- a lot of people
- false together
- different personalities
- Not meant organized
- —

TEAM

- work together
- stay together
- common Goals
- commitments
- Rules
- organized
- Supporters —

— Team Covenant —
— Pge 11 for additions —

- Flexible
- shepherd
  - Jesus come to serve not be served
- Perseverance -
- work together

_____

Logistics →

Role on the team

- Luggage →
- VBS < sports crafts → Bathrooms —
  →
- Supplies for trip
- Immulation -
- Slcit

- Pony

- Devotional

- Pre-departure coordination

Rick & Barb.

(UCHERS)

- Marriage ministry →

  ① - need to log on →

  ② - Been good check form —
  > 15 yrs old

  ③ write letter as a family →
  _____
  must hone on letter pag 23
  " Partner support section"

- Support - Prayer support : dismissed family
  —